SOL GEOMETRY

THE VIRGINIA SOL MATHEMATICS COACH, GEOMETRY

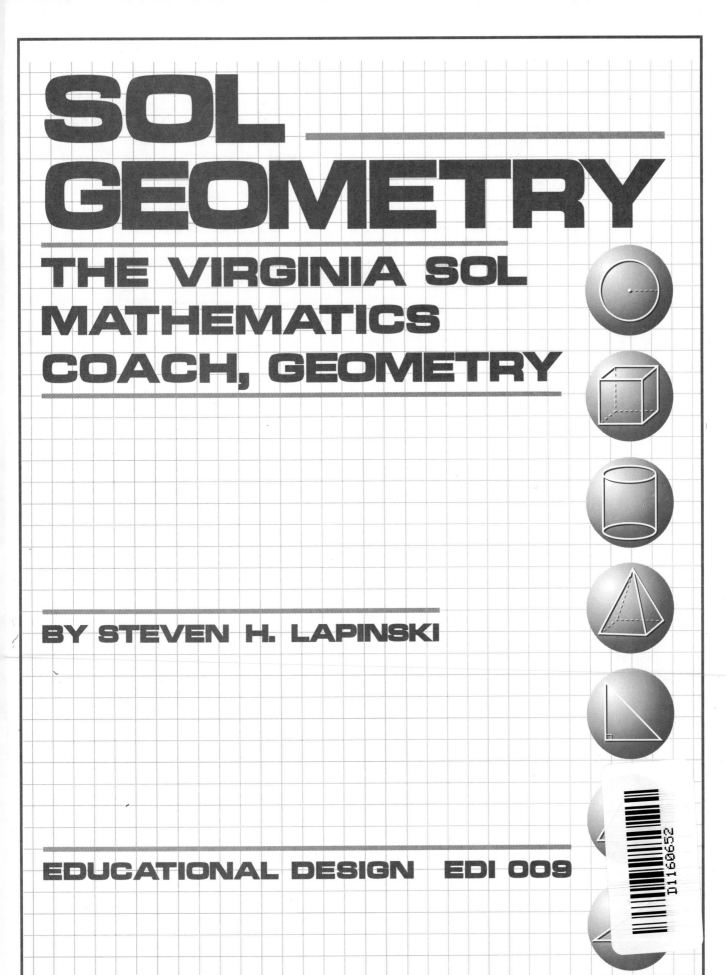

BY STEVEN H. LAPINSKI

EDUCATIONAL DESIGN   EDI 009

Mr. Steven H. Lapinski earned a B.S. degree from Pennsylvania State University and an M.Ed. degree from Beaver College. In 1985, he was the recipient of the Acro Award for Excellence in Teaching of Mathematics, awarded jointly by the School District of Philadelphia and the Acro Corporation. He taught mathematics at both middle and high schools for 16 years in Philadelphia, PA, and for the past 10 years he has served as the Mathematics Specialist for Henrico County Public Schools in Virginia. He has also worked as a consultant to other school divisions and as an adjunct instructor at colleges and universities in Pennsylvania and Virginia. Mr. Lapinski is an accomplished mathematics educator. He has acted as director of grant projects and actively participated in revising mathematics curriculum and standards. One of his professional interests is mathematics assessment, particularly at the state and local levels.

ISBN# 0-87694-965-0   EDI 009

CONTENTS

		Introduction		**4**
Unit A:		**Lines and Angles**		
	Lesson 1	Angles	*(G.3)*	7
	Lesson 2	Parallel Lines	*(G.4)*	18
	Lesson 3	Constructions	*(G.11)*	27
Unit B:		**Mathematics and Logic**		
	Lesson 4	Venn Diagrams	*(G.1)*	39
	Lesson 5	Deductive Reasoning	*(G.1)*	47
Unit C:		**Triangles**		
	Lesson 6	Triangle Inequality	*(G.6)*	54
	Lesson 7	Congruence	*(G.5)*	59
	Lesson 8	Similarity	*(G.5)*	72
	Lesson 9	Pythagorean Theorem	*(G.7)*	81
	Lesson 10	Special Right Triangles	*(G.7)*	89
	Lesson 11	Right Triangle Trigonometry	*(G.7)*	97
Unit D:		**Polygons and Circles**		
	Lesson 12	Quadrilaterals	*(G.8)*	108
	Lesson 13	Interior and Exterior Angles	*(G.9)*	116
	Lesson 14	Circles	*(G.10)*	122
Unit E:		**Three-Dimensional Figures**		
	Lesson 15	3-D Models	*(G.12)*	133
	Lesson 16	Surface Area	*(G.13)*	141
	Lesson 17	Volume	*(G.13)*	149
Unit F:		**Proportional Reasoning**		
	Lesson 18	Ratio and Proportion	*(G.14)*	156
Unit G:		**Coordinate Relations, Transformations, and Vectors**		
	Lesson 19	Distance and Midpoint	*(G.2)*	163
	Lesson 20	Slope	*(G.2)*	171
	Lesson 21	Symmetry	*(G.2)*	178
	Lesson 22	Transformations	*(G.2)*	183
	Lesson 23	Vectors	*(G.15)*	197
		Answer Sheet for PracticeTest		**208**
		PRACTICE SOL GEOMETRY TEST		**209**
		Formula Sheet		**219**

INTRODUCTION

This book will help you prepare for, and succeed on, the *Virginia SOL (Standards of Learning) Mathematics Test for Geometry.* The book provides review lessons for an entire geometry course. You will learn strategies that will help you to understand and solve problems. At the end of this book is a sample test based on the SOL Geometry Blueprint.

When you work in this book or take the SOL Geometry test, use the following helpful tips:

- **Take your time.**
  There is no time limit for this test. Rushing may lead to making careless errors.

- **Read each question carefully.**
  Read the entire question and all the answer choices. Try to analyze what the question is really asking.

- **Does your choice make sense?**
  Use your calculator or geometrical tools and try to work the problem another way to verify your answer.

- **Answer the question that is asked.**
  Some problems may require more than one step to solve. Before selecting your answer, re-read the question. Ask yourself is your answer a reasonable answer for the question asked.

- **Make "educated" guesses.**
  There is no penalty for guessing on this test. If you have forgotten how to solve a problem but can eliminate some of the choices, then make a guess.

- **Mark the correct place on the answer sheet.**
  Look at the item number and the letter of your answer choice on the test and mark the same item number and letter on the answer sheet. Make sure your answer sheet is clearly marked with dark pencil. Erase any stray marks.

- **Check your answers.**

  Before you turn your test in, check it over. Change an answer only if you have a good reason. Generally it is better to stick with your first choice.

Teachers may wish to have students take the entire sample test, or complete a portion of it followed by a class lesson before proceeding to the remaining questions. *It is important to remember that students may use graphing calculators and geometric tools on any portion of the test.* Encouraging students to use them while taking the sample test will be beneficial in prompting students to use the appropriate tools during the actual test administration.

Parents may find this book helpful in clarifying the types of questions their child will encounter on the test. Parents could also assist their child in preparing for the test by practicing at home. The list of test-taking tips gives parents suggestions on ways to reduce test anxiety and promote good study and health habits in preparation for testing.

ANGLES

SOL G.3 *The student will solve practical problems involving complementary, supplementary, and congruent angles that include vertical angles, angles formed when parallel lines are cut by a transversal, and angles in polygons.*

1 **Angles** are formed by two rays that share the same endpoint, called a **vertex**. There are 3 ways to name an angle like the one shown below.

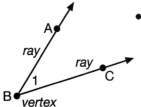

- Using a 3-letter name with the letters in this order: 1) a point on one ray, 2) the vertex, 3) a point on the other ray. In the diagram on the left, the angle could be named either $\angle ABC$ or $\angle CBA$.

- Using just the vertex letter, if there is only one angle at the vertex: $\angle B$.

- Using a number written within the angle at the vertex: $\angle 1$.

2 **Complementary angles** (shown below) are two acute angles whose measures add up to **90°**. Each angle is the **complement** of the other.

- In equation form, $m \angle QRS + m \angle SRT = 90°$. We read this equation as "The measure of angle *QRS* plus the measure of angle *SRT* is 90°."

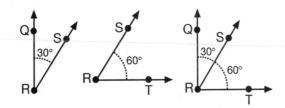

- Complements of the same angle or of **congruent** angles (angles with the same measures) are congruent. In the diagrams below, $\angle ABC$ is the complement of $\angle SRT$. $\angle QRS$ is also the complement of $\angle SRT$. So $\angle ABC$ is congruent to $\angle QRS$.

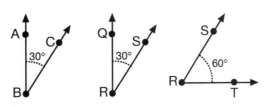

7

3 **Supplementary angles** (below) are two angles whose measures add up to **180°**. Each angle is the **supplement** of the other. Two angles that form a straight line are supplementary, so supplementary adjacent angles whose noncommon sides form a line are called a **linear pair**. In the diagram, $m \angle CBD + m \angle ABC = 180°$.

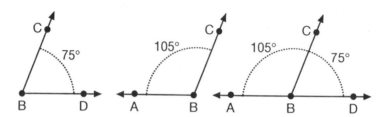

Supplements of the same angle or of congruent angles are congruent. In the diagram below, $\angle GHJ$ is the supplement of $\angle ABC$. $\angle DEF$ is also the supplement of $\angle ABC$. So $\angle GHJ$ is congruent to $\angle DEF$.

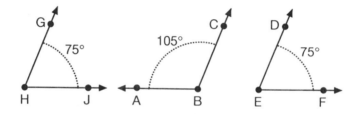

4 **Vertical Angles.** When two lines intersect, they form four angles. Angles opposite each other are called **vertical** angles, and they are congruent. In the diagram below, the vertical angle pairs are $\angle 1$ and $\angle 3$, and $\angle 2$ and $\angle 4$.

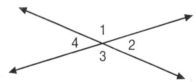

(Remember that the word *vertical*, when referring to angles, comes from the word *vertex*. It does not mean the same thing as the word *vertical* in a phrase like *a vertical line*, which means "an up-and-down line.")

5 **Adjacent** angles share one ray and the same vertex. $\angle SRT$ and $\angle VRT$ are adjacent angles because they share the same vertex (R) and the same ray (RT). The sum of the measures of the two angles formed equals the measure of $\angle SRV$. In equation form, $m\angle SRT + m\angle TRV = m\angle SRV$.

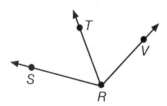

8

- Note that in the diagram of the two intersecting lines (repeated below), adjacent pairs of angles are supplementary because they form a straight line. The supplementary pairs are ∠1 and ∠2, ∠2 and ∠3, ∠3 and ∠4, and ∠4 and ∠1.

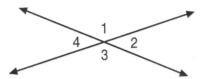

ANGLES FORMED BY TWO LINES CUT BY A TRANSVERSAL

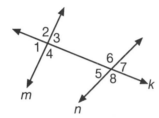

6 A **transversal** is a line that intersects two other lines. Angles formed by a transversal have special names based on their location:

- Angles 3, 4, 5, and 6 are called **interior angles.**
- Angles 1, 2, 7, and 8 are called **exterior angles.**
- NONadjacent angles on opposite sides of the transversal are called **alternate angles,** for example, ∠3 and ∠5, or ∠2 and ∠8.
  — ∠3 and ∠5 are **alternate interior angles.**
  — ∠2 and ∠8 are **alternate exterior angles.**
- **Corresponding angles** are a pair of **non**adjacent angles, one interior and one exterior, but both on the same side of the transversal—for example, ∠1 and ∠5.

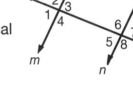

7 When a transversal crosses two **parallel lines**, the angles formed have special relationships.

- Pairs of corresponding angles are congruent.
- Pairs of alternate interior angles are congruent.
- Pairs of alternate exterior angles are congruent.

- Pairs of same-side interior angles are supplementary.
- Pairs of same-side exterior angles are supplementary.

9

ANGLES OF POLYGONS

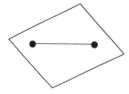

Convex polygon

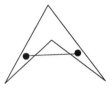

Concave polygon

8 A **convex polygon** has the following property: If you draw any segment whose endpoints are inside the polygon, all the points along the segment are also inside the polygon. A **concave polygon** does not have this property. It is possible to draw a segment whose endpoints are inside the polygon, but that contains points outside the polygon.

9 A **regular polygon** has equal angles (is **equiangular**) and equal sides (is **equilateral**).

Regular polygon

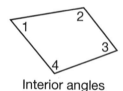

Interior angles

- The angles inside a polygon are called **interior angles.** The sum of the measures of the interior angles of a convex polygon with n sides (called an n-gon) is $(n-2)180°$.

  The measure of each angle in a regular n-gon is $\dfrac{(n-2)\,180°}{n}$

Exterior angles

- By extending each side of the polygon in either a clockwise or counter-clockwise direction, **exterior angles** are formed. The sum of the measures of the exterior angles of a convex polygon, one angle at each vertex, is 360°.

  The measure of each exterior angle in a regular n-gon is $\dfrac{360°}{n}$

10

EXAMPLE 1 What is the measure of the complement of ∠ACE?

A 63°
B 53°
C 37°
D 15°

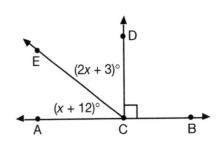

Strategy
- You know the sum of 2 complementary angles is 90°. So you need to solve the equation $(2x + 3) + (x + 12) = 90$.
- Simplify the left side. $3x + 15 = 90$
- Subtract 15 from both sides. $3x = 75$
- Divide both sides by 3. $x = 25$
- The complement of ∠ACE is ∠ECD. The measure of ∠ECD is $(2x + 3)°$. You substitute 25 for x, and simplify the expression to 53°.

Solution   Choose B.

∠D and ∠E are complementary angles. ∠D is $(x - 15)°$, and ∠E is $(x + 5)°$. What is the measure of ∠E?

EXAMPLE 2 Use the figure on the right. Which pair of angles are vertical angles?

F ∠2 and ∠5
G ∠2 and ∠3
H ∠1 and ∠2
J ∠1 and ∠8

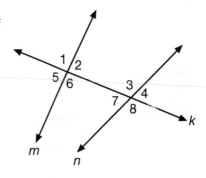

Strategy
- Choice G, ∠2 and ∠3, do not share the same vertex. Since vertical angles share the same vertex, you can eliminate this choice. You can eliminate Choice J for the same reason.
- Choice H, ∠1 and ∠2, are **adjacent** angles because they share the same ray and vertex. This eliminates choice H.

Solution
- Choose F.

11

Try It 2

Use the figure on the right. Which pair of angles are vertical angles?

F ∠LJM and ∠MJN

G ∠LJM and ∠OJN

H ∠KJL and ∠OJN

J ∠KJL and ∠LJN

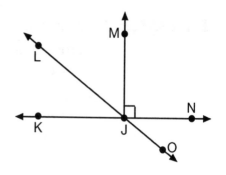

EXAMPLE 3 What is the angle relationship between ∠ABE and ∠DBE?

A vertical angles

B supplementary angles

C congruent angles

D complementary angles

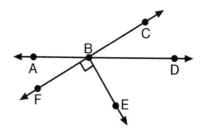

Strategy

• ∠ABE and ∠DBE are adjacent angles because they share the same vertex (*B*) and ray (*BE*).

• Also, ∠ABE and ∠DBE form a straight angle (line) *ABD*. If 2 angles form a straight line, then they are supplementary angles or a **linear pair**.

Solution

Choose B.

Try It 3

Use the figure from Example 3. What is the angle relationship between ∠ABC and ∠DBC?

A complementary angles

B congruent angles

C supplementary angles

D vertical angles

EXAMPLE 4 Use the figure on the right. What type of angles are ∠1 and ∠5?

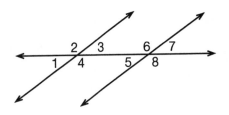

F corresponding angles

G alternate interior angles

H alternate exterior angles

J supplementary angles

Strategy

- First determine the location of ∠1 and ∠5. You can see they are on the same side of the transversal. This fact eliminates Choices G and H, since *alternate* means angles on <u>opposite</u> sides of the transversal.

- You know that same-side nonadjacent angles that are supplementary both have to be exterior angles or both interior angles.

- ∠1 is an exterior angle and ∠5 is an interior, and they are nonadjacent.

- This eliminates Choice J.

Solution Choose F.

 Use the figure on the right. What type of angles are ∠ABC and ∠BEG?

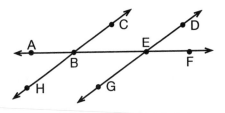

F corresponding angles

G alternate interior angles

H alternate exterior angles

J supplementary angles

EXAMPLE 5 Paul is building a clock whose face is a regular octagon. At what angle x should he cut the wood to frame the clock face?

A 45°

B 120°

C 135°

D 225°

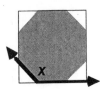

13

Strategy	• Paul is making another larger regular octagon, so he needs to use the interior angle measure.
	• The measure of each angle of a regular n–gon is $\frac{(n-2)\,180°}{n}$.
	• Replace n with 8 and simplify. $\quad \frac{(8-2)\,180°}{8} = 135°$
Solution	Choose C.

Keisha cuts a piece of glass in the form of a regular pentagon from the square pane of glass on the right. At what angle must she cut?

A 72°

B 108°

C 128°

D 300°

EXAMPLE 6 Use the figure on the right. Line m is parallel to the base of the triangle. What is the measure of $\angle A$?

F 73°

G 62°

H 45°

J 25°

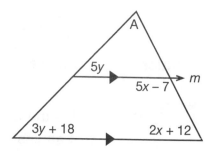

Strategy

• If the measures of 2 angles of a triangle are known, you can subtract their sum from 180 to find the measure of the third.

• $5x - 7$ and $2x + 12$ are same-side interior angles whose sum is 180°. When you solve the equation $5x - 7 + 2x + 12 = 180$, $x = 25$. The right base angle of the triangle is $2x + 12 \;\rightarrow\; 2(25) + 12 = 62°$.

• $5y$ and $3y + 18$ are corresponding angles and congruent. When you solve $5y = 3y + 18$, $y = 9$. The measure of the left base angle of the triangle is $3y + 18 \;\rightarrow\; 3(9) + 18 = 45°$.

• Solve $180 - (62 + 45) \;\rightarrow\; 180 - 107 = 73°$

14

Solution   Choose F.

Try It 6   Use the figure on the right. Line *t* is parallel to the base of the triangle. What is the measure of ∠B?

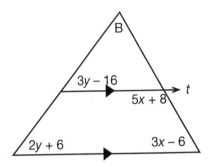

F   50°

G   60°

H   70°

J   80°

EXAMPLE 7   A ship traveling east makes a 150° turn toward the south, travels then turns due south. What is the measure of the second turn, *x*?

A   45°

B   60°

C   120°

D   135°

Strategy
- First extend the lines so you have a figure that looks like the one on the right. The turn from east to south is 90°, so ∠1 is 90°.

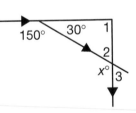

- The sum of the angles of a triangle is 180°. So 180 − (30 + 90) = 60. ∠2 is 60°.
- ∠2 and ∠3 are vertical angles, so ∠3 is 60°.
- ∠*x* and ∠3 form a linear pair—therefore their sum is 180°.
- 180° − 60° = 120°, so ∠*x* = 120°.

Solution   Choose C.

15

© Educational Design. Photocopying or reproducing any part of this book is forbidden by law.

Try It 7

Use the figure on the right. ∠1 = 2x + 2 and ∠2 = x + 32. Both are complements of ∠3. What is the measure of ∠3?

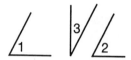

A 72°

B 62°

C 38°

D 28°

Sample Virginia SOL Questions

1. Which pair of angles are vertical angles?

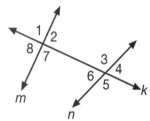

A ∠3 and ∠5

B ∠1 and ∠5

C ∠3 and ∠4

D ∠1 and ∠8

2. Lines *m* and *n* are parallel. What is the value of *x*?

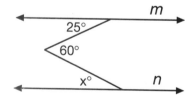

F 120°

G 80°

H 45°

J 35°

3. What is the angle relationship between ∠KJO and ∠LJK?

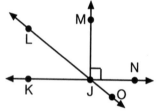

A Vertical angles

B Supplementary angles

C Congruent angles

D Complementary angles

4. Which angles are congruent?

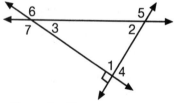

F ∠1 and ∠3

G ∠1 and ∠5

H ∠6 and ∠3

J ∠6 and ∠7

5. ∠A and ∠B are complementary angles. The measure of ∠A is (2x + 1)°, ∠B is (3x – 16)°. What is the measure of ∠B?

A   15°
B   21°
C   43°
D   47°

6. In the figure shown $\overleftrightarrow{HC} \parallel \overleftrightarrow{GD}$ and m∠ABC = 140°. Which of the following statements is false?

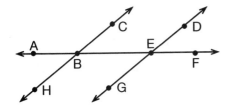

F   ∠HBF and ∠AED are alternate interior angles.

G   m∠DEF = 140°

H   ∠ABH and ∠AEG are corresponding angles.

J   m∠GEF = 140°

7. Suppose m∠ABC = 105°, what is the m∠DBC?

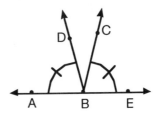

A   20°
B   30°
C   40°
D   75°

PARALLEL LINES

SOL G.4 *The student will use the relationships between angles formed by two lines cut by a transversal to determine if two lines are parallel and verify, using algebraic and coordinate methods as well as deductive proofs.*

1 To determine if two lines are parallel, you need to show or prove that one of the following angle relationships exists.

When a transversal crosses two parallel lines, the angles form—
- pairs of corresponding angles that are congruent.
- pairs of alternate interior angles that are congruent.
- pairs of alternate exterior angles that are congruent.
- pairs of same-side interior angles that are supplementary.
- pairs of same-side exterior angles that are supplementary.

2 When a transversal crosses two lines and the angles formed have any one of the above relationships, then the lines are parallel.

There are three basic ways to prove that two lines are parallel:
- using **algebraic equations**,
- using the **slope of lines** on a coordinate plane, or
- using **deductive reasoning**.

USING ALGEBRAIC EQUATIONS

EXAMPLE 1 What value of x will allow you to prove that $a \parallel b$?

    ($a \parallel b$ is read "line a is parallel to line b")

A 160

B   90

C   45

D   25

a $2x + 70$

b $4x - 20$

Strategy   • First determine the relationship between the angles, and use that relationship to create an equation.

- $\angle(2x + 70)$ and $\angle(4x - 20)$ are corresponding angles which are congruent. You can write an equation with one equal to the other and solve for x. $4x - 20 = 2x + 70$
- Move the variables to one side: $4x - 2x = 70 + 20$
- Simplify: $2x = 90$ $x = 45$
- Verify by substituting in the original: $4(45) - 20 = 2(45) + 70$

$$180 - 20 = 90 + 70$$
$$160 = 160$$

Solution   Choose C.

Try It 1

What value of y will make $a \parallel b$?

A 12.7

B 13

C 14

D 44.5

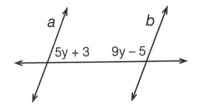

EXAMPLE 2 Which property, illustrated by the diagram, justifies the statement that $m \parallel n$?

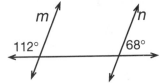

F a pair of supplementary same-side interior angles

G a pair of congruent alternate interior angles

H a pair of congruent alternate exterior angles

J a pair of same-side exterior angles that are supplementary

Strategy
- You need to determine the location of the angles. The angles are on the **same side** of the transversal and are **exterior** (on the outside of the lines). Since $112° + 68° = 180°$, they are **supplementary same-side exterior angles**.
- You can eliminate Choice G and H, since alternate angles are on opposite sides of the transversal.
- You can eliminate Choice F, since the angles are not interior.

Solution   Choose J.

19

Try It 2

Which statement justifies that $a \parallel b$?

F A pair of congruent corresponding angles.

G A pair of congruent alternate interior angles.

H A pair of supplementary same-side interior angles.

J A pair of supplementary same-side interior angles.

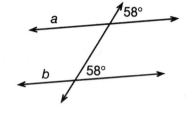

EXAMPLE 3 Lines p and m are cut by transversal t. Angles 2 and 8 are alternate interior angles. $m\angle 2 = 3x + 16$ and $m\angle 8 = 8x - 24$. What value of x makes $p \parallel m$?

(HINT: Whenever a question does not come with a diagram, it often helps for you to draw the diagram yourself and label it.)

A 40

B 16

C 8

D −8

Strategy

- Alternate interior angles are congruent, so you can write an equation of one angle equal to the other, then solve for x: $\qquad 3x + 16 = 8x - 24$
- Move the variables to the same side $\quad 3x - 8x = -24 - 16$
- Simplify $\qquad\qquad\qquad\qquad\qquad -5x = -40$
- Solve by dividing both sides by -5 $\qquad x = 8$

Solution

Choose C.

Try It 3

Lines p and m are cut by transversal t. Angles 1 and 7 are alternate exterior angles, $m\angle 1 = 3x - 34$ and $m\angle 7 = 2x + 21$. What value of x makes $p \parallel m$?

A 11

B 13

C 45

D 55

20

PARALLEL LINES ON THE COORDINATE PLANE

3 A line on a coordinate plane can be described by its steepness or **slope**. Here's a quick review:

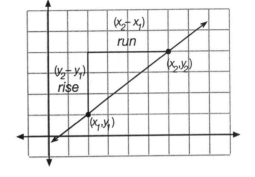

- The slope of a line is the ratio of the units the line changes vertically (**rise**) to the units the line changes horizontally (**run**).

- In equation form,

$$\text{slope} = \frac{\text{change in } y \text{ (vertical distance)}}{\text{change in } x \text{ (horizontal distance)}}$$

$$\text{slope} = \frac{\text{rise}}{\text{run}}$$

$$\text{slope} = \frac{y_2 - y_1}{x_2 - x_1}$$

- Parallel lines have the same slope.

- If two lines are perpendicular (intersect and form 90° angles), then the product of the slopes of the two lines is –1. (*Exception*: lines parallel to the x- and y- axes. They have no product that can be determined.)

EXAMPLE 4 What is the slope of the line in the diagram above?

Strategy
- You can see just by glancing at the diagram that the rise is 2 and the run is 3, so that the slope ($\frac{\text{rise}}{\text{run}}$) is $\frac{2}{3}$. But you should learn how to get this result by using equations alone:

- Look at the coordinates of the two points on the diagram (x_1,y_1) and (x_2,y_2). The coordinates are (1,1) and (4,3).

- The **rise** is $y_2 - y_1$. Since $y_2 = 3$ and $y_1 = 1$, then the rise is $3 - 1 = 2$.
- The **run** is $x_2 - x_1$. Since $x_2 = 4$ and $x_1 = 1$, then the run is $4 - 1 = 3$.

Solution The slope is $\dfrac{\text{rise}}{\text{run}} = \dfrac{2}{3}$.

Try It 4 ▶ What is the slope of a line that contains points at (0,2) and (3,5)?

(If you think you need more review than this, go to Lesson 20 on Slope.)

21

EXAMPLE 5 Points A (-4,27), and B (2,3) are on $\overleftrightarrow{AB}$. Which line is parallel to $\overleftrightarrow{AB}$?

    A $C(-2,2)$, $D(0,6)$ on $\overleftrightarrow{CD}$

    B $E(-3,7)$, $F(2,-13)$ on $\overleftrightarrow{EF}$

    C $R(-3,5)$, $T(-1,1)$ on $\overleftrightarrow{RT}$

    D $G(-2,5)$, $H(0,6)$ on $\overleftrightarrow{GH}$

Strategy

- You need to find the slope of $\overleftrightarrow{AB}$ and for each answer choice. The choice with the same slope as $\overleftrightarrow{AB}$ is parallel to $\overleftrightarrow{AB}$.

- To start: the slope of $\overleftrightarrow{AB}$ is $\frac{27-3}{-4-2}$ = $\frac{24}{-6}$ = $\frac{-4}{1}$ = -4

- Choice A: The slope of $\overleftrightarrow{CD}$ is $\frac{2-6}{-2-0}$ = $\frac{-4}{-2}$ = $\frac{2}{1}$ = 2

- Choice B: The slope of $\overleftrightarrow{EF}$ is $\frac{7-(-13)}{-3-2}$ = $\frac{20}{-5}$ = $\frac{-4}{1}$ = -4

- You can stop here and select your answer. There will be only one pair that will be parallel.

Solution   Choose G.

Try It 5

Points $A(-4,0)$, $B(-2,1)$ are on $\overleftrightarrow{AB}$. Which line is parallel to $\overleftrightarrow{AB}$?

    A $C(0,1)$, $D(3,7)$ on $\overleftrightarrow{CD}$

    B $E(-3,-6)$, $F(0,-3)$ on $\overleftrightarrow{EF}$

    C $R(2,-8)$, $T(5,-17)$ on $\overleftrightarrow{RT}$

    D $G(2,-5)$, $H(4,-4)$ on $\overleftrightarrow{GH}$

4 A common way to wite the equation of a line is the **slope-intercept** form: $y = mx + b$. In this form, m is the slope of the line, and b is the y-intercept—the point where the line crosses the y-axis.

EXAMPLE 6 Which equation defines a line that is parallel to the given line $x + y = -5$ and passes through the given point $(5, -2)$?

    F $y = -x + 3$

    G $y = x + 3$

    H $y = -x - 7$

    J $y = x - 7$

22

Strategy

There are two strategies that you can use:

- **STRATEGY 1.** First take the original equation ($x + y = -5$), and solve it for y (the slope-intercept form):

  $x + y = -5 \quad \rightarrow \quad y = -x - 5$.

  Eliminate choices that do not have the same slope (–1).

  — G and J do not have the same slope (their slope is 1), so the lines cannot be parallel.

  Next, take the x-value of the given point (5). Substitute it in each of the remaining equations (F and H) and solve for y. If the statement equals the y-value of the given point (–2), then the line passes through the point and is parallel to the given line $x + y = -5$.

  Choice F: $y = -x + 3 \quad \rightarrow \quad y = -(5) + 3 \rightarrow y = -2$.
  Choice H: $y = -x - 7 \quad \rightarrow \quad y = -(5) - 7 \rightarrow y = -12$.

- **STRATEGY 2.** Take the original equation ($x + y = -5$) and solve it for y (the slope intercept form). $x + y = -5 \quad \rightarrow \quad y = -x - 5$. You can eliminate choices G and J that do not have the same slope (–1), . Using a graphing calculator, enter the equations of the remaining choices (F and H) into the tables menu and enter the x-value (5). The equation with the y-value of –2 is the parallel line.

Solution

Choose F.

> **Try It 6**

Which equation defines a line that is parallel to the given line $y = 4x - 3$ and that passes through the given point (0,2)?

F $y = 4x + 2$
G $y = 4x - 1$
H $y = 4x + 3$
J $y = 4x$

EXAMPLE 7 Which pair of linear equations represents two lines that are perpendicular?

A $y = \frac{1}{3}x + 2$ and $y = 3x - 7$

B $y = \frac{1}{3}x + 2$ and $y = -x + 5$

C $y = \frac{1}{3}x - 1$ and $y = -3x + 5$

D $y = \frac{2}{3}x - 1$ and $y = -3x + 5$

Strategy
- For each choice, find the products of each slope. If the product of the slopes is −1, then the lines are perpendicular.
- Choice F: $\frac{1}{3} \cdot 3 = 1$
- Choice G: $\frac{1}{3} \cdot 1 = \frac{1}{3}$
- Choice H: $\frac{1}{3} \cdot -3 = -1$
- Choice J: $\frac{2}{3} \cdot 3 = -2$
- The product of the slopes of Choice C is −1, so these lines are perpendicular.

Solution Choose H.

Try It 7

Which pair of linear equations represents two perpendicular lines?

A $y = \frac{1}{3}x + 2$ and $y = 3x + 1$

B $y = \frac{-1}{5}x - 1$ and $y = 5x + 2$

C $y = \frac{-2}{3}x + 2$ and $y = \frac{-3}{2}x + 5$

D $y = \frac{3}{4}x - 7$ and $y = \frac{4}{3}x - 2$

TRY IT Answers: *1. B*   *2. F*   *3. D*   *4. 1*   *5. D*   *6. F*   *7. B*

1. Points $A(0,-3)$ and $B(2,3)$ are on $\overleftrightarrow{AB}$. Which line is parallel to $\overleftrightarrow{AB}$?

   A $C(0,2)$, $D(2,3)$ on $\overleftrightarrow{CD}$

   B $E(1,-2)$, $F(5,8)$ on $\overleftrightarrow{EF}$

   C $G(1,5)$, $H(4,14)$ on $\overleftrightarrow{GH}$

   D $R(0,5)$, $T(3,2)$ on $\overleftrightarrow{RT}$

2. The figure shows the plans for the roof of a house and its garage. The front rafters of the garage and house are to be parallel. What must be true about $\angle 1$ and $\angle 2$ for the rafters to be parallel?

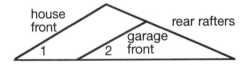

   F A pair of congruent corresponding angles.

   G A pair of congruent alternate interior angles.

   H A pair of congruent alternate exterior angles.

   J A pair of supplementary same-side interior angles.

3. What is the value of x which will allow you to prove that $\overleftrightarrow{AB} \parallel \overleftrightarrow{CD}$ when $m\angle F = 144°$ and $m\angle E = (3x - 30)°$?

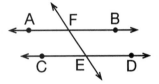

   A 22

   B 36

   C 58

   D 66

4. Which pair of lines are parallel?

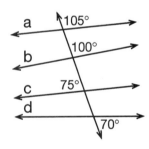

   F $a \parallel b$

   G $a \parallel d$

   H $c \parallel d$

   J $a \parallel c$

5. Which theorem or postulate justifies that $a \parallel b$?

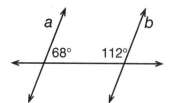

A A pair of congruent alternate interior angles

B A pair of supplementary same-side exterior angles

C A pair of supplementary same-side interior angles

D A pair of congruent corresponding angles

6. Lines p and m are cut by transversal t. Angles 2 and 8 are alternate interior angles, $m\angle 2 = 20x - 14$, and $m\angle 8 = 7x + 103$. What value of x makes $p \parallel m$?

F $x = 9$

G $x = 63$

H $x = 166$

J $x = 180$

7. Which of the following statements is **FALSE**?

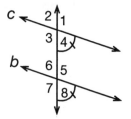

A $b \parallel c$

B Angles 4 and 8 are corresponding angles.

C If $m\angle 4 = 72°$, then $m\angle 7 = 108°$

D Angles 2 and 5 are alternate interior angles.

8. A line parallel to a given line $2x - y = 6$ passes through $(-4, -5)$ and which other point?

F $(-1,1)$

G $(-4,0)$

H $(-1,-5)$

J $(-1,4)$

CONSTRUCTIONS

SOL G.11 *The student will construct, using a compass and straightedge, a line segment congruent to a given line segment, the bisector of a line segment, a perpendicular to a given line from a point not on the line, a perpendicular to a given line at a point on the line, the bisector of a given angle, and an angle congruent to a given angle.*

1 To draw mathematical figures that require exactness, a **construction** (a specialized type of drawing) is used. In a construction, you can only use two tools. They are the straightedge (unmarked) and the compass.

- The **straightedge** is a tool with a straight edge. It is unmarked because specific lengths are not used in a construction. A ruler is often used as a straightedge, but you may not use the measurements on the ruler.

- A **compass** is a tool used to draw circles, (not the kind used to determine direction North-South).

2 In a construction, these four rules apply.

- A point must either be given, or be the intersection of previously constructed figures.

- If a figure is given, you can assume as many points as necessary to make that figure.

- A straightedge can draw a line, named $\overleftrightarrow{AB}$, through two points A and B.

- A compass can draw a circle with the center at A and containing a second point B on its circumference.

TO CONSTRUCT AN ANGLE BISECTOR

1. Place the compass point at the vertex, *B*. With the center at *B*, draw an arc that intersects the sides of the angle. Label the points of intersection *X* and *Y*. See figure 1.

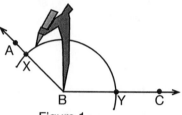

Figure 1

2. Place the compass point at *X* and draw an arc in the interior of ∠*ABC*. Place the compass point at *Y*. Using the same radius, draw an arc that intersects the previous arc. See figure 2.

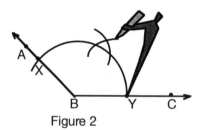

Figure 2

3. Label the point of intersection *Z*. Draw $\overrightarrow{BZ}$, which is the angle bisector of ∠*ABC*. See figure 3. ∠*ABZ* ≅ ∠*CBZ*

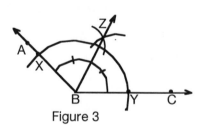

Figure 3

28

TO CONSTRUCT AN ANGLE CONGRUENT TO A GIVEN ANGLE

1. To copy ∠ABC (figure 1), place the compass point at the vertex, *B*. With the center at *B*, draw an arc that intersects the sides of the angle. Label the points of intersection *D* and *E*. See figure 2.

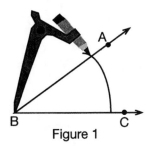

Figure 1

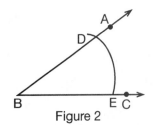

Figure 2

2. Draw a new line *m* and mark a point *P* on the line. Place your compass point at *P*. Use the same radius that you used in Step 1, and draw an arc with its center at *P* that intersects line *m*. Label the intersection point *Q*. See figure 3.

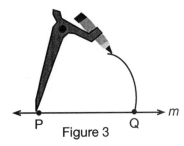

Figure 3

3. On the original angle, measure $\overset{\frown}{ED}$ with your compass (see figure 4). Then, on line *m,* place your compass point at *Q*. Use a radius equal to $\overset{\frown}{ED}$, draw an arc with center at *Q*. Label the intersection point of the two arcs *R*. See figure 5.

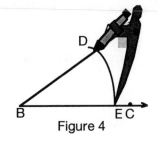

Figure 4

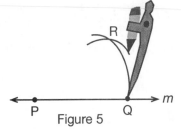

Figure 5

4, Draw $\overrightarrow{PR}$. The measure of ∠RPQ is the same as the measure of ∠ABC.

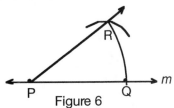

Figure 6

29

TO CONSTRUCT A PERPENDICULAR BISECTOR

1. Place the compass point on point *A*. Use a radius that is more than half the length of $\overline{AB}$. Draw an arc that intersects $\overline{AB}$. See figure 1.

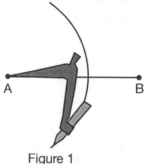

Figure 1

2. Using the same radius, place the compass point at *B*, (see figure 2) and draw an arc that intersects the previous arc BOTH above and below $\overline{AB}$. Label the intersection points of the arcs *P* and *Q*. See figure 3.

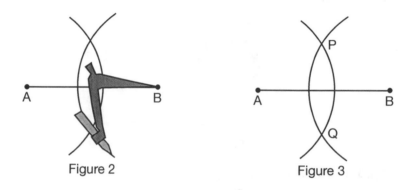

Figure 2   Figure 3

3. Draw $\overleftrightarrow{PQ}$, which is the perpendicular bisector of $\overline{AB}$ (see figure 4). The diagram shows *PQ* as a line, $\overleftrightarrow{PQ}$, which bisects $\overline{AB}$.

   You can use this construction to find the midpoint of any line segment.

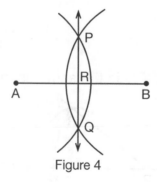

Figure 4

30

TO CONSTRUCT A PERPENDICULAR LINE THROUGH A POINT ON A LINE

1. To draw a perpendicular to line *m* at point *P*, first place the compass point at *P*. Draw 2 arcs of the same radius, one on either side of *P*, that intersect line *m*. Label the points of intersection *A* and *B*. See figure 1.

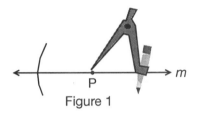

Figure 1

2. Place the compass point at *A*. Use a radius greater than the previous one, and draw an arc above with center at *A*. Place the compass point at *B*. Using the same radius, draw an arc with the center at *B* that intersects the previous arc. See figure 2.

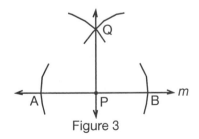

Figure 2

3. Label the point of intersection of the 2 arcs *Q*. Draw $\overleftrightarrow{PQ}$, which is perpendicular to *m*. See figure 3.

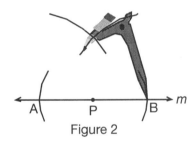

Figure 3

TO CONSTRUCT A PERPENDICULAR LINE THROUGH A POINT OFF A LINE:

1. To draw a line perpendicular to line m through point P, first place the compass point at P. Draw an arc that intersects line m at 2 points. See figure 1.

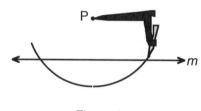

Figure 1

2. Label the intersection points S and T. Place the compass point at T. Using any radius longer than half the distance between S and T, draw an arc with center at T on the opposite side of the line from P. See figure 2.

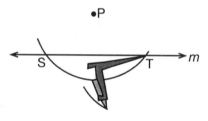

Figure 2

3. Repeat this same step from point S, using the same radius. Label the intersection point of the 2 arcs Q. Draw $\overleftrightarrow{PQ}$, which is perpendicular to line m. See figure 3.
$\overleftrightarrow{ST} \perp \overleftrightarrow{PQ}$

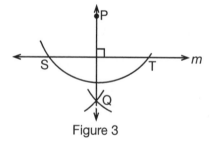

Figure 3

32

EXAMPLE 1 Given ∠ACE, use your compass and straightedge to construct the adjacent ∠A'CE, so that ∠A'CE includes $\overrightarrow{CE}$ and ∠A'CE ≅ ∠ACE. Which point lies on ∠A'CE?

A W
B X
C Y
D Z

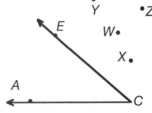

Strategy There are two methods you can use to solve this problem.

- You can use the procedure to copy an angle given earlier in this lesson. You will use $\overrightarrow{EC}$ for the base of your copied angle. The constructed ray will contain one of the points.

- You can use an informal method sometimes used for demonstration purposes in math classes. It is a paper-folding technique, in which you use tracing paper or new patty paper (the food service paper used to separate sliced cheese or hamburger). Patty paper comes in 4-inch squares. Trace ∠ACE and all the points of the figure on the paper. Fold the paper exactly along $\overrightarrow{CE}$ and crease. $\overrightarrow{CA}$ will intersect with point W, which lies on ∠A'CE.

Solution Choose A.

Given ∠ABC, use your compass and straightedge to construct ∠ABC' so that ∠ABC ≅ ∠ABC'. Which point lies on ∠ABC'?

A W
B X
C Y
D Z

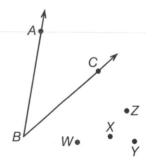

EXAMPLE 2 Given ∠ABC, use your compass and straightedge to construct an angle bisector of ∠ABC.

Which point lies on the angle bisector of ∠ABC?

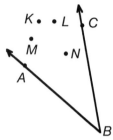

F K
G L
H M
J N

Strategy   There are two ways to bisect an angle.

- You can use the procedure to bisect an angle given earlier in this lesson.
- You can use a paper folding technique. Trace ∠ACE and the points on the paper. Fold the paper so that $\overline{AB}$ folds onto $\overline{BC}$, and point B is on the fold. The crease in the paper will go through point *K,* which is on the angle bisector.

Solution   Choose F.

Try It 2   Use the figure on the right, and with your compass and straightedge construct an angle bisector of ∠ABC.

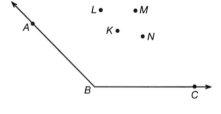

Which point lies on the angle bisector of ∠ABC?

F K
G L
H M
J N

EXAMPLE 3 Given $\overline{AB}$, use your compass and straightedge to construct a perpendicular bisector so that $\overline{AP} \cong \overline{PB}$.

Which point lies on the bisector?

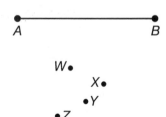

A W
B X
C Y
D Z

34

Strategy   There are two methods for constructing a perpendicular bisector.

- You can use the procedure to construct a perpendicular bisector given earlier in this lesson.
- You can use a paper folding technique, and trace $\overline{AB}$ and all the points (choices) on the paper. Fold the paper, point A onto point B. The crease in the paper will be the perpendicular bisector and will go through point Y.

Solution   Choose C.

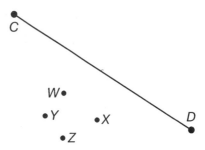

Given $\overline{CD}$ on the right, use your compass and straightedge to construct a perpendicular bisector so that $\overline{CP} \cong \overline{PD}$. Which point lies on the perpendicular bisector?

A   W
B   X
C   Y
D   Z

EXAMPLE 4 Use the figure on the right, along with your compass and straightedge, to construct a perpendicular line through point E on $\overline{DF}$. Which point lies on the perpendicular to $\overline{DF}$?

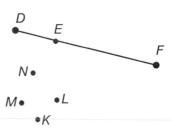

F   K
G   L
H   M
J   N

Strategy   There are two methods for constructing a perpendicular through a point on the line.

- You can use the procedure to construct a perpendicular through a point on the line given earlier in this lesson, using a compass and straightedge.

35

- You can use a paper folding technique. Trace $\overline{DF}$ and all the points on the paper. Fold the paper so that point D is on $\overline{DF}$, and the crease of the fold is through point E. The fold will go through point K and will be perpendicular to $\overline{DF}$.

Solution   Choose F.

 Use the figure on the right, along with your compass and straightedge, to construct a perpendicular line at point X on $\overline{WY}$. Which point lies on the perpendicular to $\overline{WY}$?

F K
G L
H M
J N

EXAMPLE 5 Use the figure on the right, along with your compass and straightedge, to construct a perpendicular line from $\overline{AB}$ to point E. Which point on $\overline{AB}$ is on the perpendicular?

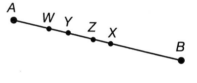

A W
B X
C Y
D Z

Strategy   There are two methods for constructing a perpendicular through a point not on the line.
- You can use the procedure given earlier in this lesson to construct a perpendicular through a point not on the line, using a compass and straightedge.
- Using a paper folding technique, you trace $\overline{AB}$ and all the points on the paper. Fold the paper so that point A is on $\overline{AB}$ and the crease of the fold is through point E. The fold will go through point Y and will be perpendicular to $\overline{AB}$.

Solution   Choose C.

Try It 5

Use the figure on the right with your compass and straightedge to construct a perpendicular line from $\overline{BC}$ to point D. Which point on $\overline{BC}$ is on the perpendicular?

A   W
B   X
C   Y
D   Z

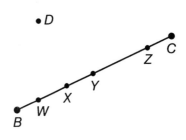

Sample Virginia SOL Questions

1. Given $\angle DEF$, use your compass and straightedge to construct $\angle DEF'$ so that $\angle DEF \cong \angle DEF'$.

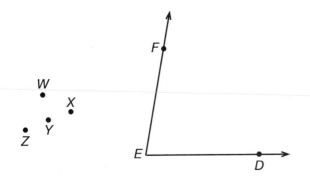

Which point lies on $\angle DEF'$?

A   W
B   X
C   Y
D   Z

2. Given $\overline{AB}$ below, use your compass and straightedge to construct a $\perp$ so that $\overline{AP} \cong \overline{PB}$. Which point lies on the perpendicular bisector?

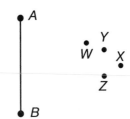

F   W
G   X
H   Y
J   Z

3. Use the figure below and your compass and straightedge to construct an angle bisector of ∠1. Which point lies on the angle bisector of ∠1?

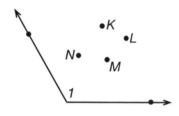

A K
B L
C M
D N

4. Use the figure below and your compass and straightedge to construct a perpendicular line from $\overline{AB}$ to point C. Which point on $\overline{AB}$ is on the perpendicular?

• C

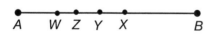

F W
G X
H Y
J Z

5. Use the figure below and your compass and straightedge to construct a perpendicular line through point H on $\overline{GJ}$. Which point lies on the perpendicular line?

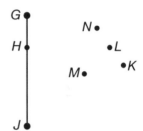

A K
B L
C M
D N

VENN DIAGRAMS

SOL G.1   *The student will construct and judge the validity of a logical argument consisting of a set of premises and a conclusion. This will include diagramming arguments involving quantifiers (all, no, none, some), using Venn diagrams.*

The use of diagrams can make what appears to be a difficult problem rather easy. You can use a special kind of diagram called a **Venn diagrams** to show logic statements in diagram form.

1   In a Venn diagram there is a rectangular figure which shows the **universal set**, that is, the most inclusive set among those under consideration. Circles or ovals within the rectangular figure show subsets of the universal set. If animals were the universal set then dogs, cats, and birds would be subsets of the universal set, but lawn mowers would not.

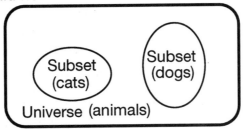

2   Venn diagrams show three basic relationships:

- **Disjoint** – non-overlapping circles. Objects represented in one loop have nothing in common with objects in the second loop. Statements with the words *"no"* or *"none"* often describe disjoint relationships such as "No triangles are squares." See figure 1 on the right.

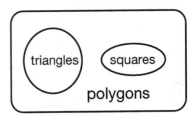

Fig. 1. Disjoint

- **Overlapping** (Intersecting) – represents objects with characteristics common to the sets of objects. Statements with the word *"some"* often describe overlapping relationships such as "Some roses are red." Also, the relationship can be a part of a larger group. "Some flowers are roses" See figure 2 below.

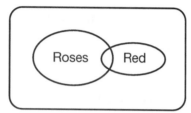
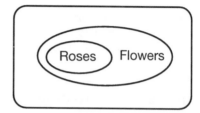

Fig. 2a. Overlapping   Fig. 2b. Part of Larger Group

- **Subset** (Enclosed) – when one loop completely encloses another, the inner loop represents a subset of the outer loop. Statements with the word *"all"* often describe subset relationships such as "All rectangles are four-sided". See figure 3 on the right. Thus, in Figure 2b, above, the diagram shows "All roses are flowers" as well as "Some flowers are roses."

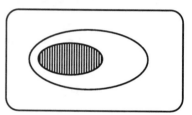

Fig. 3. Subset (Enclosed)

3 There are different zones in a Venn diagrams, and each represents different attributes that the objects have or don't have. Look at the figure below and the list of possible characteristics for each zone.

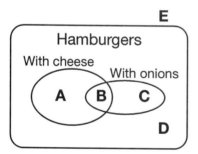

A – Hamburger with cheese, no onions.
B – Hamburger with cheese and onions.
C – Hamburger with onions, no cheese.
D – Hamburger, no cheese, no onions.
E – Not hamburger.

4 **True** vs. **Valid**—two words often used in logic. *True* means something close to what it means in everyday speech. *Valid* means only "correctly reasoned." It's possible for a conclusion to be valid but untrue: *Trees have wings, and my uncle is a tree, therefore my uncle has wings.* The conclusion is valid (correctly reasoned), even though the first two statements and the conclusion are totally untrue. Computer programmers refer to this as GIGO—"Garbage in, garbage out." But if the statements are true **and** the reasoning valid, the conclusion will be true.

EXAMPLE 1 Which Venn diagram represents the following statement?

All high school teachers are college graduates.

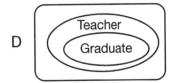

A

B

C

D

Strategy

- The statement contained the word "All" which indicates that the correct choice should be a subset or enclosed diagram like Choices C and D.

- Teachers represent a portion of all college graduates. This makes them a subset of all college graduates.

- Therefore you would choose C.

Solution Choose C.

Try It 1

Which Venn diagram represents the following statement?

All rectangles (R) are quadrilaterals (Q).

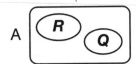

A

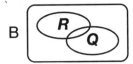

B

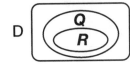

C

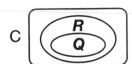

D

EXAMPLE 2 Of the following statements based on the Venn diagram on the right, which statement is valid? (You don't have to know what an arachnid is to answer the question.)

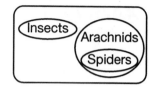

F All arachnids are spiders.

G Some arachnids are spiders.

H Some spiders are arachnids.

J All spiders are insects.

Strategy
- First, look at each choice and compare the statement to the diagram.

- Choice F: The diagram shows that spiders are a subset of arachnids because the spiders' loop is contained in the arachnids' loop. You can eliminate choice F, because the diagram shows you that <u>not all</u> arachnids are spiders.

- Choice G: The diagram shows that not all arachnids are spiders, because arachnids contain spiders with space left over for other creatures. This means <u>some</u> arachnids <u>are</u> spiders, and you can choose G.

Solution
Choose G.

(And in case you were wondering, arachnids are a class of animals that includes scorpions, ticks, and daddy-longlegs as well as spiders.)

Try It 2

Of the following statements based on the Venn diagram on the right, which statement is valid?

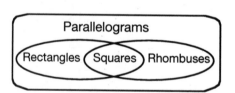

F Some parallelograms are squares.

G All rectangles are squares.

H All parallelograms are rectangles.

J Some squares are rhombuses.

5 A Venn diagram can be a useful tool for visually displaying logic statements. A **conditional statement**, *"IF P THEN Q"*, can be displayed as "All the points in region *P* that are also in region *Q*." For example, the diagram below right displays the following statement:

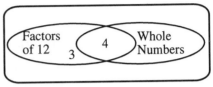

IF 3 is a factor of 12, THEN there is a whole number which multiplied by 3 yields the product 12.

The *"IF"* part is the **given,** or **hypothesis**, and the *"THEN"* part is the **conclusion.**

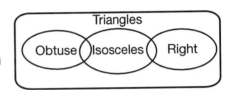

EXAMPLE 3 Which conditional statement, below, is represented by the Venn diagram on the right?

    A If a triangle is right, then it is isosceles.

    B If a triangle is isosceles, then it is obtuse.

    C If a triangle is right, then it is not obtuse.

    D If a triangle is obtuse, then it is isosceles.

Strategy

- First, look at each choice and compare the statement to the diagram. If you can find one example that is false, then the whole statement is false. This is called a counter-example.

- Choice A: A triangle could be a right triangle and not have two sides that are equal, such as a 3, 4, 5, right triangle. This is a **counter-example** and eliminates this choice.

- Choice B: An isosceles triangle has base angles that are equal. A triangle could have angles of 50, 50, and 80. None of these angles is obtuse. You can eliminate choice B.

- Choice C: A right triangle has one angle of 90° and two angles whose sum is 90°. An obtuse angle is greater than 90°, so a right triangle cannot be obtuse. This is a true statement.

Solution   Choose C.

Try It 3 ▶ Which conditional statement below, is represented by the Venn diagram on the right?

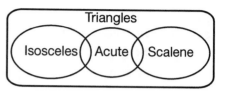

A If a triangle is isosceles then it is acute.

B If a triangle is acute then it is isosceles.

C If a triangle is scalene then it is not isosceles.

D If a triangle is acute then it is not scalene.

EXAMPLE 4 Which of the following Venn diagrams illustrates that the reasoning below is not valid?

All mailmen (M) are rich. Some rich (R) people are thin (T). Therefore, no mailman is thin.

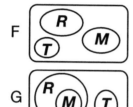

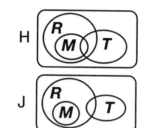

Strategy

• First, look at each choice and compare the statement to the diagram. A diagram that contains the statement "*All mailman (M) are rich*" must have **M** enclosed by **R**. You can eliminate choice F, where **M** is <u>outside</u> **R**.

• A diagram for the second statement "*Some rich people (R) are thin*" must show **R** and **T** overlapping. **R** and **T** do NOT overlap in choice G, so it, too, can be eliminated. This leaves only H and J.

• <u>Both</u> H and J show "*All mailmen (M) are rich. Some rich (R) people are thin (T)*." But the placement of T differs in the two answer choices.

— J illustrates the situation where no mailmen are thin, as the original statement says.

— But H illustrates the counter-example where some mailmen <u>are</u> thin. And it's a perfectly valid alternative way of diagramming the statements.

44

- But if the reasoning were truly valid, it could not produce two different Venn diagrams. Diagram H shows a possible conclusion that is different from the conclusion in the original statement. Diagram H shows where the reasoning is not valid.

Solution   Choose H.

Try It 1   Which of the following Venn diagrams illustrates that the reasoning below is not valid?

All banana trees (B) have green leaves. That plant has green leaves (G). Therefore that plant is a banana tree.

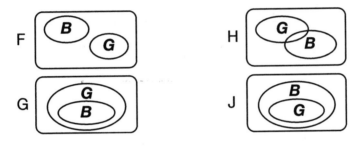

TRY IT! Answers: **1. D   2. F   3. C   4. G**

1. Which of the following Venn diagrams shows that the following reasoning is valid?

   All rainy days are cloudy. Today is not cloudy. Therefore today is not rainy.

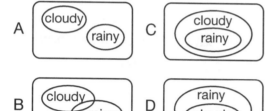

2. Which Venn diagram represents the following statement?

   Some students go to the beach.

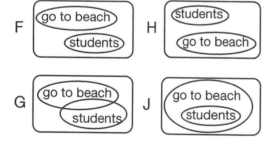

3. Of the following statements based on the Venn diagram below, which is true?

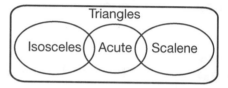

   A All isosceles triangles are acute.
   B Some isosceles triangles are scalene.
   C All acute triangles are scalene.
   D Some scalene triangles are acute.

4. Which conditional statement below is represented by the following Venn diagram?

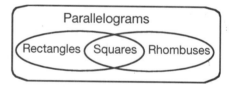

   F If a parallelogram is a rhombus then it is a square.
   G If a parallelogram is rectangle then it is a square.
   H If a parallelogram is square then it is a rectangle.
   J If a parallelogram is a rectangle then it is a rhombus.

DEDUCTIVE REASONING

SOL G.1 *The student will construct and judge the validity of a logical argument consisting of a set of premises and a conclusion. This will include—*
- *identifying the converse, inverse, and contrapositive of a conditional statement.*
- *translating a short verbal argument into symbolic form.*
- *using valid forms of deductive reasoning, including the law of syllogism.*

1 Geometry is based on a logical (deductive) system in which conclusions are justified by means of previously assumed or proved statements.

2 Every deductive structure contains the following four elements:

— **Undefined terms** are described but not defined. (*Example*: point, line)

— **Postulates** or **unproved assumptions** (*Example*: If two lines intersect, then they intersect in exactly one point.)

— **Definitions** (*Example*: *If* a point is the midpoint of a segment, *then* the point divides the segment into two congruent segments.)

A definition is always reversible—*If* a point divides a segment into two congruent segments, *then* the point is the midpoint of the segment.

— **Theorems** or proved conclusions. (*Example*: Vertical angles are congruent.)

3 Definitions are always reversible (*see above*); postulates and theorems may or may not be reversible.

4 Some statements are in the form of "if *p*, then *q*." This form is called a **conditional statement**, where *p* is the statement that you know is true (**hypothesis**), and *q* is the statement that you conclude is true (**conclusion**).

Conditional Statement

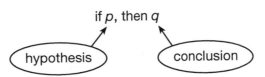

The symbol form of "if *p*, then *q*" is $p \Rightarrow q$ and is read "*p implies q*." In a proof it is important to know *p*, what is given, and *q*, what is to be proved.

5 The **negation** of a statement "It is snowing," is "It is not snowing," and can be written as ~p.

6 There are three other kinds of statements associated with each conditional statement, "if p then q." For example, take the conditional statement "If you live in Richmond, then you live in Virginia."

- The **converse** of a statement switches the hypothesis and conclusion. A converse statement would be "If you live in Virginia, then you live in Richmond" (if q then p, or q ⇒ p). The converse of a statement may or may not be true. (In this example, it is clearly not true.)

- The **inverse** of a statement is the negation of both the hypothesis and conclusion. An inverse statement would be "If you do not live in Richmond, then you do not live in Virginia" (if ~p then ~q or ~p ⇒ ~q). The inverse of a statement may or may not be true. (Again, in this example, it is clearly not true.)

- The **contrapositive** of a statement combines the converse and the inverse— that is, it is the negation of the converse of the statement. A contrapositive statement would be "If you do not live in Virginia, then you do not live in Richmond" (if ~q then ~p or ~q ⇒ ~p). The contrapositive of a statement has the same truth value as the statement. If p, then q ⇔ if ~q then ~p. (In this case, since the original example is true, the contrapositive is also true.)

Statement $p \Rightarrow q$	Converse $q \Rightarrow p$	Inverse $\sim p \Rightarrow \sim q$	Contrapositive $\sim q \Rightarrow \sim p$
If two angles are right angles, then they are congruent. *TRUE*	If two angles are congruent, then they are right angles. *FALSE*	If two angles are not right angles, then they are not congruent. *FALSE*	If two angles are not congruent, then they are not right angles. *TRUE*

7 When a conditional statement and its converse are both true, you can combine them into a **biconditional** statement. For example, the statement, "if two angles are congruent, then they have the same measure" and its converse "if two angles have the same measure, then they are congruent" are both true.

8 A biconditional statement can be shortened by using "*if and only if*" as in "Two angles are congruent, *if and only if*, they have the same measure."

EXAMPLE 1 The converse of which of the following statements is true?

    A If a figure is a square, then it is a rectangle.

    B Rain $\Rightarrow$ Wet

    C If an angle is 45°, then it is acute.

    D If a triangle is equilateral, then it is equiangular.

Strategy
- Construct the converse of each statement by starting with the "*then*" part and following with the "*if*" part. Then see if it is true.

- Choice A: It is possible for a figure to be a rectangle and not a square. This eliminates choice A.

- Choice B: It is possible to be wet (swimming) and not raining. This eliminates choice B.

- Choice C: It is possible for an angle to be acute (30°) and not be 45°. This eliminates choice C.

- Choice D: If a triangle has equal angles (60°), then it has equal sides.

Solution   Choose D.

The converse of which of the following statements is true?

    A If you travel from the United States to Spain, then you have a passport.

    B If two nonvertical lines are parallel, then their slopes are equal.

    C If a polygon is a square, then its sides are congruent.

    D If it is snowing outside, then it is cold outside.

EXAMPLE 2 Which of the following is the contrapositive of $p \Rightarrow \sim q$?

    F $\sim p \Rightarrow q$

    G $\sim q \Rightarrow p$

    H $q \Rightarrow \sim p$

    J $\sim q \Rightarrow \sim p$

Strategy
- The contrapositive is the negation of the converse of the statement, so start with the converse and then negate it. The converse statement is $\sim q \Rightarrow p$, and this eliminates choice F.

- The negation of the converse, $\sim q \Rightarrow p$, is $\sim\sim q \Rightarrow \sim p$, which simplifies to $q \Rightarrow \sim p$. This eliminates choices G and J.

Solution   Choose H.

Try It 2   Which of the following is the contrapositive of $\sim u \Rightarrow w$?

    F $\sim w \Rightarrow u$

    G $\sim w \Rightarrow \sim u$

    H $w \Rightarrow \sim u$

    J $u \Rightarrow \sim w$

EXAMPLE 3 The inverse of which of the following statements is true?

    A If M is the midpoint of $\overline{AB}$, then M, A, and B are collinear.

    B If a polygon is a rectangle, then it is a quadrilateral.

    C If an angle is acute, then it has a measure greater than 0° and less than 90°.

    D If each side of a triangle has a length of 10, then its perimeter is 30.

Strategy
- The inverse is the negation of both parts of the conditional statement. Add the word *not* to each part, and then evaluate the new statement. You need only to find one counterexample to show that a statement is false.

- Choice A: If M is *not* the midpoint of $\overline{AB}$, then M, A, and B are *not* collinear. False: M, A, and B still could be collinear (on the same line), and another point could be the midpoint.

- Choice B: If a polygon is *not* a rectangle, then it is *not* a quadrilateral. False: a polygon could be a parallelogram that is a quadrilateral but not a rectangle.

- Choice C: If an angle is *not* acute, then it does *not* have a measure greater than 0° and less than 90°. True, because an angle that is not acute will have a measure of 90° or greater.

- Choice D: If each side of a triangle does *not* have a length of 10, then its perimeter is *not* 30. False, a triangle with sides of 5, 12, and 13 has a perimeter of 30.

Solution   Choose C.

Try It 3   The inverse of which of the following statements is false?

A   If a polygon is a triangle, then it has three sides.

B   If two angles are congruent, then they have equal measures.

C   If two angles are right angles, then they are congruent.

D   If the sum of the measures of two angles is 90°, then the angles are complementary.

EXAMPLE 4 Which is the concluding statement for the following chain of reasoning?

$$p \Rightarrow \sim q$$
$$r \Rightarrow q$$
$$s \Rightarrow r$$

F $s \Rightarrow \sim p$

G $r \Rightarrow \sim p$

H $s \Rightarrow \sim q$

J $r \Rightarrow \sim q$

Strategy

- First find the letter (or phrase) that is both a hypothesis for one statement and a conclusion for another statement. This is the letter r.

- Next, rearrange the statements in sequence so that the conclusion r leads to the hypothesis r: $s \Rightarrow r$, $r \Rightarrow q$

- To complete the chain, you need to change the statement $p \Rightarrow \sim q$ to its contrapositive form of $q \Rightarrow \sim p$.

- The chain of reasoning is $s \Rightarrow r$, $r \Rightarrow q$, $q \Rightarrow \sim p$. This can be simplified to $s \Rightarrow \sim p$.

Solution   Choose F.

Try It 4

Which is the concluding statement for the following chain of reasoning?

$a \Rightarrow b$ $b \Rightarrow f$

$d \Rightarrow \sim c$ $\sim c \Rightarrow a$

F $b \Rightarrow f$

G $d \Rightarrow \sim f$

H $b \Rightarrow \sim c$

J $d \Rightarrow f$

TRY IT! Answers: *1. B*   *2. F*   *3. C*   *4. J*

Sample Virginia SOL Questions

1. Which of the following is the contrapositive of ~k ⇒ ~h?

   A k ⇒ h
   B h ⇒ ~k
   C h ⇒ k
   D ~h ⇒ ~k

2. The converse of which of the following statements is NOT true?

   F If two angles are adjacent, then they have a common side.

   G If an angle is acute, then it is not obtuse.

   H If two lines in the same plane do not intersect, then they are parallel.

   J If an angle has a measure of 90°, then its sides are perpendicular.

3. Which is the concluding statement for the following chain of reasoning?

   g ⇒ e
   ~t ⇒ w
   t ⇒ ~e

   A g ⇒ ~w
   B g ⇒ w
   C t ⇒ w
   D t ⇒ ~w

4. The inverse of which of the following statements is true?

   F If two angles are vertical then they are congruent.

   G If the outer rays of two adjacent angles form a straight angle, then the angles are supplementary.

   H If an angle measures 120°, then it is obtuse.

   J If an angle is a right angle, then its measure is not 20°.

5. What conclusion can be drawn from the following?

   ~c ⇒ ~f
   g ⇒ b
   p ⇒ f
   c ⇒ ~b

   A p ⇒ ~g
   B p ⇒ g
   C g ⇒ ~f
   D g ⇒ f

TRIANGLE INEQUALITY

SOL G.6 *The student, given information concerning the lengths of sides and/or measures of angles, will apply the triangle inequality properties to determine whether a triangle exists and to order sides and angles. These concepts will be considered in the context of practical situations.*

1 To form a triangle, you need three sides, and the sum of any two sides must be greater than the third side. If the sum of any two sides is not greater, then you cannot form a triangle. This relationship is stated as the **Triangle Inequality Theorem**:

$$\overline{XY} + \overline{YZ} > \overline{XZ} \qquad \overline{YZ} + \overline{XZ} > \overline{XY} \qquad \overline{XZ} + \overline{XY} > \overline{YZ}$$

2 You can order the sides of triangles from smallest to largest. The largest side is opposite the largest angle, and the smallest side is opposite the smallest angle.

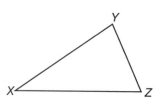

3 Conversely, if one side of a triangle is longer than another side, then the angle opposite the longer side is larger than the angle opposite the shorter side.

4 The third side of a triangle has to be greater than the differences of the other 2 sides. (That is, the sum of any two sides must be greater than the third.)

EXAMPLE 1 A bicycle designer is cutting steel tubing for the triangular section (*ABC*) for this bicycle. Two sections 18 in. and 24 in. are cut. Which inequality best expresses the range of possible measure of the third side?

A $6 < x < 42$

B $6 < x < 24$

C $18 < x < 42$

D $18 < x < 24$

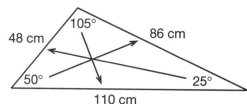

54

Strategy
- The third side of a triangle has to be greater than the differences of the other 2 sides and less than their sum.
- The difference of the 2 sides is 24 − 18 = 6. This eliminates choices C and D.
- The sum of the 2 sides is 24 + 18 = 42. This eliminates choice B.

Solution   Choose A.

Try It 1   Two sides of a triangle are 10 cm and 11 cm long. Which inequality best expresses the range of the measure of the third side, x?

A $1 < x < 21$

B $1 < x < 12$

C $10 < x < 21$

D $0 < x < 9$

EXAMPLE 2 A shelf is to be supported with brackets as shown on the right. What is a possible width for the shelf?

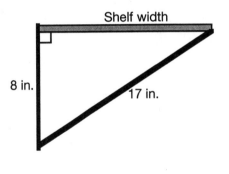
Shelf width
8 in.
17 in.

F   7 in.

G   9 in.

H   15 in.

J   25 in.

Strategy
- The shelf width has to be greater than the difference of the 2 known sides:

  17 - 8 = 9 inches. You can eliminate choices F and G, since they are not greater than 9.

- The sum of any two sides of a triangle must be greater than the third. So the shelf is less than the sum of the 2 known sides:

  17 + 8 = 25 inches. You can eliminate choice J, since it is not less than 25.

Solution   Choose H.

(Another way to find the width: Use the Pythagorean Theorem: $8^2 + x^2 = 17^2$; $x = 15$)

Try It 2 ▶ Which is a possible side for this triangle?

    F   4

    G   7

    H 18

    J   20

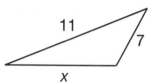

EXAMPLE 3 There is a triangle formed by the tubing on the bicycle shown on the right. Which angles are arranged from smallest to largest?

    A ∠1, ∠2, ∠3

    B ∠2, ∠1, ∠3

    C ∠2, ∠3, ∠1

    D ∠3, ∠2, ∠1

Strategy

- You know that the smallest angle is opposite the smallest angle. The side of 49 cm is the smallest and the angle opposite it is ∠2.

- Therefore choices A and D are eliminated, because ∠2 is not listed as the smallest angle.

- The next smallest side is 58 cm, and the angle opposite it is ∠3. This eliminates choice B.

Solution   Choose C.

Try It 3 ▶ A builder is designing a triangular deck. She wants to place benches in the two largest corners. In which corners should she place the benches?

    A 1, 2

    B 1, 3

    C 2, 3

    D 3, 1

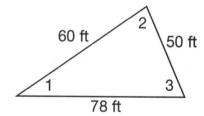

56

EXAMPLE 4 In the diagram on the right, which is the longest side?

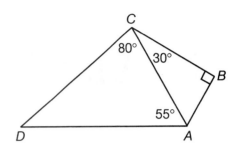

F $\overline{AC}$

G $\overline{AD}$

H $\overline{CB}$

J $\overline{DC}$

Strategy

- Keep in mind that the longest side of a triangle is opposite the largest angle, and that the sum of the angles of a triangle is 180°

- Let's look at the triangles one at a time.

  — In △ABC, the given angles are 90° and 30°. So the third angle must be 60° (90° + 30° + 60° = 180°). The largest angle in the triangle, therefore, is the right angle. (In fact, the largest angle in any right triangle is the right angle.) And the longest side is $\overline{CA}$, the side opposite it.

  — Similarly, in △ACD, the missing angle D must be 45°. (80° + 55° + 45 ° = 180°) Since this is the smallest angle, this makes the side opposite it, $\overline{AC}$, the smallest side of △ACD.

- Since $\overline{AC}$ is largest side of △ABC but it is the smallest side of △ACD, it eliminates choice F.

- $\overline{AD}$ is opposite the largest angle in △ACD. It is the largest side and is larger than any side in △ABC.

Solution   Choose G.

In the diagram on the right, which is the longest side?

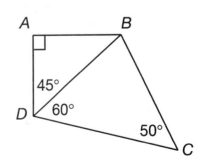

F $\overline{DB}$

G $\overline{BC}$

H $\overline{AB}$

J $\overline{DC}$

57

Sample Virginia SOL Questions

1. By airplane the distance from Richmond to Roanoke is 146 miles and it's 82 miles from Norfolk to Richmond. Which inequality expresses the distance, m, from Norfolk to Roanoke?

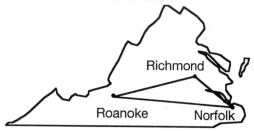

A   82 miles $< m <$ 146 miles

B   63 miles $< m <$ 228 miles

C   64 miles $< m <$ 228 miles

D   228 miles $< m <$ 64 miles

2. In the diagram below, which is the longest side?

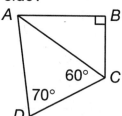

F $\overline{AC}$

G $\overline{AD}$

H $\overline{DC}$

J $\overline{AB}$

3. Susan has two landscaping timbers that have lengths of 4.8 ft. and 3.4 ft. A third piece of timber is to be used with these two as a border for a triangular flower bed. Which length is correct for the third piece?

A   8 ft.

B   8.2 ft.

C   8.6 ft.

D   9 ft.

4. Look at the crane below. What is the minimum length, in feet, of the cable $\overline{AB}$?

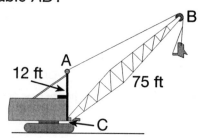

F   87 ft.

G   86 ft

H   64 ft

J   63 ft

58

CONGRUENCE

SOL G.5 *The student will—*
- *investigate and identify congruence relationships between triangles.*
- *prove two triangles are congruent given information in the form of a figure or statement, using algebraic and coordinate as well as deductive proofs.*

1 Two triangles are **congruent** (equal in measure) (≅) if corresponding angles are congruent (equal in measure) and corresponding sides are congruent (equal in length).

2 It is not necessary to show congruence of all 3 pairs of angles and 3 pairs of sides to prove congruence of two triangles. You can prove congruence of two triangles by showing congruence of certain 3 sets of parts:

- **SAS**: *Side-Angle-Side*—Two sides and the included angle of one triangle are congruent to the corresponding two sides and included angle of the second triangle.

- **SSS**: *Side-Side-Side*—Three sides of one triangle are congruent to the corresponding three sides of the second triangle.

- **ASA**: *Angle-Side-Angle*—Two angles and the included side of one triangle are congruent to the corresponding two angles and included side of the second triangle.

- **AAS**: *Angle-Angle-Side*—two angles and a non-included side of one triangle are congruent to the corresponding two angles and non-included side of the second triangle.

3 Two "properties" are often used in proving triangles congruent:

- The **reflexive property**, or property of identity, says that something is equal to (or congruent to) itself. For example: 4 = 4; ∠ABC = ∠ABC; etc.

- The **transitive property**, in its simplest form, says that two things equal to a third are equal to each other. If both a = c and b = c, then a = c. Similarly, if $\overline{AB} \cong \overline{CD} \cong \overline{EF}$, then $\overline{AB} \cong \overline{EF}$.

4 It is important that you do not make any assumptions based on the diagram given with your problem. You should not assume that lines are parallel, or angles are right angles, or segments are congruent, unless this is explicitly stated as given or marked on the figure.

5 A **proof** is a convincing argument that starts with given facts and, through logical reasoning, leads to a valid conclusion.

Let's look at three styles of doing the same deductive proof.

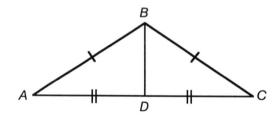

The median of an isosceles triangle
bisects the angle opposite the base.

Given: △ABC is an isosceles triangle and $\overline{BD}$ is a median (a segment bisecting the base of the triangle.)

Prove: ∠ABD ≅ ∠CBD

- **Two-Column Proof:** The statements and reasons are organized into two separate columns:

Statements	Reasons
△ABC is an isosceles triangle	Given
$\overline{BD}$ is a median	Given
$\overline{AB} \cong \overline{CB}$	Definition of isosceles triangle
$\overline{AD} \cong \overline{CD}$	Definition of median
$\overline{BD} \cong \overline{BD}$	Reflexive Property
△ABD ≅ △CBD	SSS
∠ABD ≅ ∠CBD	Corresponding Parts of Congruent Triangles are Congruent (CPCTC)

- **Paragraph Proof:** Statements and reasons are connected in complete sentences:

    Since $\triangle ABC$ is an isosceles triangle, then $\overline{AB} \cong \overline{BC}$. $\overline{BD}$ is a median, which means $\overline{AD} \cong \overline{CD}$. Since $\overline{BD}$ is shared by both $\triangle ABD$ and $\triangle CBD$, you know that the two triangles are congruent by SSS. Therefore, $\angle ABD \cong \angle CBD$ because corresponding parts of congruent triangles are congruent.

- **Flow Proof:** The logical connections between statements are shown through the use of a flowchart diagram.

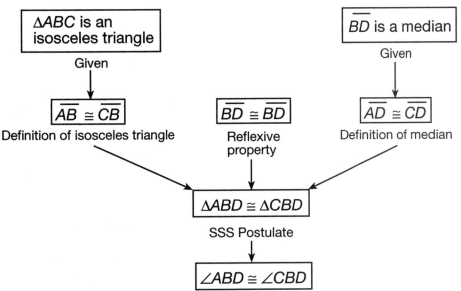

EXAMPLE 1 Given the diagram below with $\angle 1 \cong \angle 3$ and $\angle 2 \cong \angle 4$, which of the following statements is true?

A $\triangle ABD \cong \triangle DBC$

B $\triangle ABD \cong \triangle CDB$

C $\triangle DBA \cong \triangle CDB$

D $\triangle BAD \cong \triangle DBC$

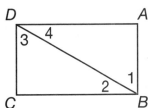

Strategy

- The two triangles are congruent by ASA, with $\overline{DB}$ the included side.

- The order of the letters *always* indicates the corresponding vertices, so you must find the pairs of corresponding vertices then match their order.

- $\angle A$ corresponds with $\angle C$, $\angle 1$ to $\angle 3$, and $\angle 2$ to $\angle 4$.

- Choice A: Vertex A does not match with vertex D. Therefore, you can eliminate this choice.

- Choice B: Vertex A does match with vertex C and the order of the other angles, $\angle 1$ and $\angle 4$ match $\angle 3$ and $\angle 2$. This is a true statement.

Solution   Choose B.

Try It 1

Which of the following statements is true based on the figure?

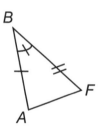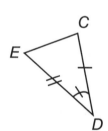

A $\angle FBA \cong \angle DEC$

B $\angle BFA \cong \angle EDC$

C $\angle ABF \cong \angle CED$

D $\angle BFA \cong \angle DEC$

EXAMPLE 2 Which of the following statements about the two triangles below is true?

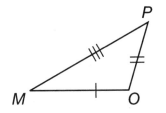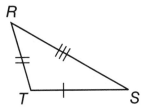

F   △MOP ≅ △RST by SSS

G   △POM ≅ △STR by SAS

H   △MOP ≅ △STR by SSS

J   △MPO ≅ △SRT by ASA

Strategy
- Since all the corresponding sides of the two figures have congruence marks and the angles are not marked, you can prove these triangles congruent by SSS. This eliminates choices G and J.

- The corresponding vertices are M and S, O and T, and P and R. The order of vertices in choice F do not match. This eliminates choice F.

- The order of vertices in choice H do match and therefore is the correct choice.

Solution   Choose H.

Try It 2   Use the figure below. Which correctly completes the statement? "△ABC ≅ _____ , by _____ ."

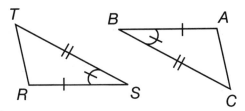

F   △TSR, SAS

G   △RST, SAS

H   △SRT, ASA

J   △RST, SSS

EXAMPLE 3 Which correctly completes the statement?

To prove $\triangle ABC \cong \triangle STU$ by ASA, you must show that $\angle B \cong$ ___ , $\overline{BC} \cong$ ___ , and $\angle C \cong$ ___ .

A $\angle T, \overline{UT}, \angle S$

B $\angle S, \overline{ST}, \angle U$

C $\angle T, \overline{TU}, \angle U$

D $\angle T, \overline{ST}, \angle U$

Strategy
- The corresponding vertices are A and S, B and T, and C and U, so $\angle B$ corresponds to $\angle T$, $\angle C$ corresponds to $\angle U$, and $\overline{BC}$ corresponds to $\overline{TU}$.

- There is only one choice that matches the two angles and one segment, and that is choice C.

Solution   Choose C.

Try It 3   Which correctly completes the statement? To prove $\triangle PQR \cong \triangle XYZ$ by SAS, you must show that $\overline{PQ} \cong$ ___ , $\angle Q \cong$ ___ , and $\overline{QR} \cong$ ___ .

A $\overline{XY}, \angle Z, \overline{XZ}$

B $\overline{XY}, \angle Y, \overline{YZ}$

C $\overline{XZ}, \angle Y, \overline{XY}$

D $\overline{XZ}, \angle X, \overline{YZ}$

EXAMPLE 4 In the diagram below, $\overline{AD} \parallel \overline{CB}$ with $\angle A \cong \angle C$. What postulate or theorem would prove $\triangle ADB \cong \triangle CBD$?

F SSS
G ASA
H SAS
J AAS

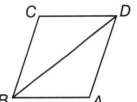

Strategy

- From the given, $\overline{AD} \parallel \overline{CB}$, you can deduce that $\angle ADB \cong \angle CBD$ because they are alternate interior angles. Also you are given another pair of congruent angles. Choices F and H can be eliminated, since they don't use two angles.

- The side that can be proved congruent is $\overline{BD} \cong \overline{BD}$ because of the reflexive property. (That is, the side is equal to, or congruent to, itself.) This is not the included side between the angles, therefore choice G is eliminated.

- AAS would be used to prove the triangles congruent.

Solution   Choose J.

In the diagram at right, $\overline{AB} \parallel \overline{CD}$, $\angle B \cong \angle D$ and $\overline{AB} \cong \overline{CD}$. What postulate or theorem would prove $\triangle ABF \cong \triangle CDE$?

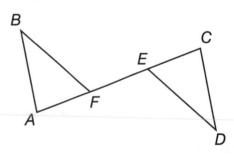

F ASA
G SSS
H SAS
J AAS

65

EXAMPLE 5 Given: $\angle R \cong \angle T$, $\overline{RV} \cong \overline{TW}$, and S is the midpoint of $\overline{RT}$.

Prove: $\triangle VRS \cong \triangle WTS$.

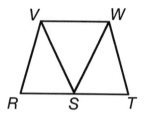

What postulate or theorem would complete this flow proof?

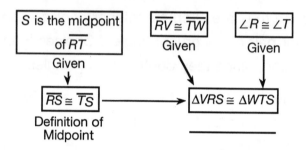

A   SSS

B   SAS

C   ASA

D   AAS

Strategy

• You are given a pair of congruent angles and sides. The proof shows another pair of congruent sides.

• From the information provided in the proof, you can only prove the triangles congruent by SAS.

Solution   Choose B.

Try It 5 Given: $\overline{NP} \cong \overline{QR}$, $\overline{PR} \cong \overline{NQ}$ Prove: $\angle N \cong \angle R$

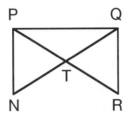

Which postulates or theorems would complete this proof?

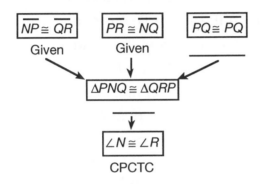

A   Reflexive, SSS

B   Reflexive, SAS

C   Transitive, SSS

D   Transitive, SAS

CONGRUENCE OF RIGHT TRIANGLES

6   You can prove congruence of two right triangles by showing congruence of certain pairs of parts.

- **HL: *Hypotenuse-Leg***—The hypotenuse and leg of one right triangle are congruent to the corresponding hypotenuse and leg of a second right triangle. This is a special case for right triangles. The right angles are the corresponding congruent angles.

- **HA: *Hypotenuse-Acute Angle***—The hypotenuse and acute angle of one right triangle are congruent to the corresponding hypotenuse and acute angle of a second right triangle. This is a special form of AAS, since the right angle represents the other angle.

- **LL:** *Leg-Leg*—The 2 legs of one right triangle are congruent to the corresponding 2 legs of a second right triangle. This is a special form of SAS, since the right angle is between the legs.

- **LA:** *Leg-Acute Angle*—The leg and acute angle of one right triangle are congruent to the corresponding leg and acute angle of a second right triangle. This is a special form of ASA, since the right angle represents the other angle.

EXAMPLE 6 A TV antenna pole ($\overline{OP}$) is perpendicular to the plane of a roof. (In the three-dimensional drawing at right, both angles at O are right angles.) If the guy wires $\overline{AP}$ and $\overline{BP}$ are congruent, prove that A and B must be the same distance from O. Which postulate or theorem would complete this proof?

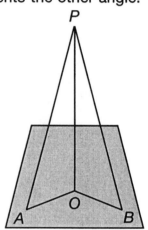

Statements	**Reasons**
1. $\overline{AP} \cong \overline{BP}$	1. Given
$\overline{PO} \perp \overline{AO}$	
$\overline{PO} \perp \overline{BO}$	
2. $\overline{PO} \cong \overline{PO}$	2. Reflexive Prop.
3. $\triangle POA \cong \triangle POB$	3. ?
4. $\overline{AO} \cong \overline{BO}$	4. CPCTC

F HA

G HL

H LA

J LL

Strategy

- Since you do not know anything about the acute angles you can eliminate choices F and H.

- The guy wire is the hypotenuse of the triangle and the wires are congruent. The antenna pole is a leg of a right triangle. This is enough information to prove the triangles congruent by hypotenuse-leg (HL).

Solution Choose G.

68

Try It 6 ▶ A circular saw blade is made by cutting out triangles from a regular heptagon. If $\overline{AB}$ is cut the same length for each tooth, prove that all the triangles removed will be congruent. Which postulate or theorem would complete this proof?

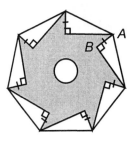

F   HA

G   HL

H   LA

J   LL

EXAMPLE 7 Which triangles are congruent in the given coordinate system?

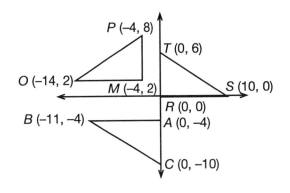

A $\triangle ABC \cong \triangle RST$

B $\triangle MOP \cong \triangle RST$

C $\triangle MOP \cong \triangle ABC$

D   all three triangles

Strategy
- To determine the lengths of each side of each triangle, you can use either the distance formula or the Pythagorean theorem. The triangles with ALL three sides congruent are congruent by SSS.

- The distances are
  $m\overline{RS} = 10$, $m\overline{RT} = 6$, and $m\overline{ST} = \sqrt{136}$ or about $11\frac{2}{3}$
  $m\overline{MO} = 10$, $m\overline{MP} = 6$, and $m\overline{OP} = \sqrt{136}$ or about $11\frac{2}{3}$
  $m\overline{AB} = 11$, $m\overline{AC} = 6$, and $m\overline{BC} = \sqrt{157}$ or about $12\frac{1}{2}$

- Only $\triangle RST$ and $\triangle MOP$ have all three sides congruent, so by SSS the two triangles are congruent.

Solution   Choose B.

Try It 7

Which triangles are congruent in the given coordinate system?

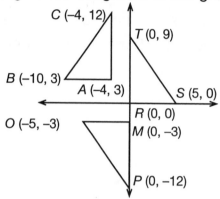

A $\triangle MOP \cong \triangle ABC$

B $\triangle RST \cong \triangle ABC$

C $\triangle MOP \cong \triangle RST$

D All three triangles

TRY IT Answers: 1. D   2. G   3. B   4. F   5. A   6. G   7. C

Sample Virginia SOL Questions

1. Given the diagram below, $\overline{AB} \cong \overline{CD}$ and $\angle 1 \cong \angle 3$, which of the following statements is true?

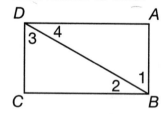

A $\triangle BAD \cong \triangle DBC$

B $\triangle DBA \cong \triangle CDB$

C $\triangle ABD \cong \triangle CDB$

D $\triangle ABD \cong \triangle DBC$

2. Use the figure below. Which correctly completes the statement?

"$\triangle ABC \cong$ _____ , by _____ ."

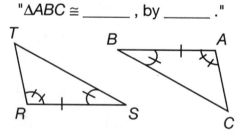

F $\triangle RST$, ASA

G $\triangle TSR$, AAS

H $\triangle RST$, AAS

J $\triangle STR$, ASA

70

3. Which correctly completes the statement? To prove $\triangle ABC \cong \triangle PQR$ by ASA, you must show that $\angle B \cong$ ___ , $\overline{BC} \cong$ ___ , and $\angle C \cong$ ___ .

A $\angle Q, \overline{PQ}, \angle R$

B $\angle R, \overline{QR}, \angle Q$

C $\angle Q, \overline{QR}, \angle R$

D $\angle P, \overline{PQ}, \angle Q$

4. In the diagram below, $\angle T \cong \angle V$ and E is the midpoint of TV. What postulate or theorem would prove $\triangle TEB \cong \triangle VEC$?

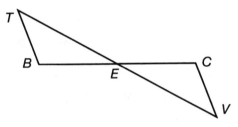

F SSS

G AAS

H ASA

J SAS

5. Which triangles are congruent in the given coordinate system?

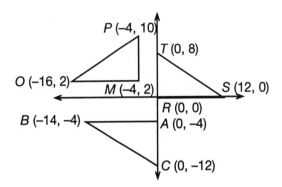

A $\triangle MOP \cong \triangle RST$

B $\triangle ABC \cong \triangle RST$

C $\triangle MOP \cong \triangle ABC$

D all three triangles

71

SIMILARITY

SOL G.5 *The student will—*
- *investigate and identify similarity relationships between triangles.*
- *prove two triangles are similar given information in the form of a figure or statement, using algebraic and coordinate as well as deductive proofs.*

1 Two or more polygons are **similar** if (1) corresponding angles are congruent, and (2) the ratios of their corresponding sides are equal.

2 Two triangles are similar if—

- three sides of one triangle are *proportional* to three sides of the other triangle. This is the **Side-Side-Side similarity theorem**. (SSS~)

- two sides of one triangle are *proportional* to two sides of the other triangle and the included angles are *congruent*. This is the **Side-Angle-Side similarity theorem**. (SAS~)

- two angles of one triangle are *congruent* to two angles of the other triangle. This is the **Angle-Angle similarity theorem** (AA~).

EXAMPLE 1 Which of the following statements *must* be true?

    A All parallelograms are similar.

    B All rectangles are similar.

    C All squares are similar.

    D All pentagons are similar.

Strategy
- In order for two polygons to be similar, their corresponding angles must be congruent. But it is possible for two parallelograms to have angles of different measures. One parallelogram's angle measures might be 80°, 100°, 80°, and 100°, and another's 60°, 120°, 60°, and 120°. This eliminates choice A.

- In order for two polygons to be similar, the ratios of their corresponding sides must be equal. But it is possible for two rectangles, for example, to have ratios of their sides that are not equal. Think of a square and a long, thin rectangle. A rectangle whose sides are 3 and 6 is not similar to a rectangle with sides of 5 and 8 because the ratios $\frac{3}{5} \neq \frac{6}{8}$. This eliminates choice B.

- All squares do have congruent angles—they are all 90°. And since a square is a regular polygon (quadrilateral), all its sides are equal. A square whose sides measure x is similar to a square with sides y because the ratios $\frac{x}{y} = \frac{x}{y}$.

- All pentagons are not similar, since their sides do not always have to be equal.

Solution   Choose C.

Try It 1

Which of the following statements *must* be true?

A Any two rectangular prisms are similar.

B Any two cubes are similar.

C Any two triangular prisms are similar.

D Any two cylinders are similar.

EXAMPLE 2 A simple instrument for measuring heights is made from a movable 4-inch rod that can slide along a ruler. You are 20 ft. from a tree and the moveable rod is 5 inches from your eye. What is the tree's height?

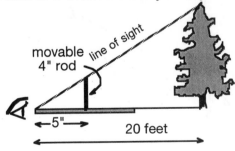

F 16 ft

G 24 ft

H 25 ft

J 28 ft

73

Strategy
- By AA, the triangle formed by the rod, rule, and line of sight is similar to the larger triangle formed by the tree, rule, and line of sight. Therefore their sides are proportional.

$$\frac{20}{5} = \frac{\text{height of tree}}{4}$$

- Cross multiply and solve for the height: $4 \cdot 20 = \text{height} \cdot 5$.

- The height of the tree $= \dfrac{4 \cdot 20}{5} = 16$ feet.

Solution   Choose F.

Try It 2

A light source is 40 ft. from a wall. How far away from the light must a 6-ft. person stand so that the person's shadow is 8 ft. tall?

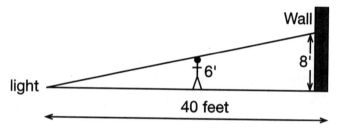

F   20 ft

G   24 ft

H   30 ft

J   53.3 ft

EXAMPLE 3 Given: $\overline{AD}$ is parallel to $\overline{BC}$, and $\overline{AB}$ and $\overline{DC}$ intersect at point O. Which of the following statements is true?

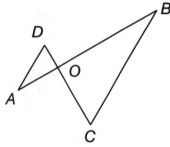

A   △AOD ~ △BOC by AA

B   △AOD is not similar to △BOC

C   △AOD ~ △BOC by SSS

D   △AOD ~ △BOC by SAS

74

Strategy

- Since $\overline{AD} \parallel \overline{BC}$, then $\angle DAB \cong \angle CBA$ and $\angle ADC \cong \angle BCD$ because they are alternate interior angles. Therefore the triangles $\triangle AOD \sim \triangle BOC$ by AA. This eliminates choice B.

- Choices C and D are eliminated because you are given nothing about the sides of the triangles.

Solution   Choose A.

Try It 3

Given: $\triangle ABC$ and $\triangle TMC$, $\angle CMT \cong \angle B$, $\overline{CM} = 2$, $\overline{CT} = 3$, and $\overline{TB} = 1$. Which of the following statements is true?

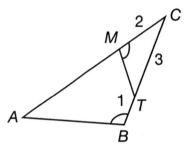

A $\triangle ABC \sim \triangle TMC$ by SAS~

B $\triangle ABC \sim \triangle TMC$ by AA~

C $\triangle ABC \sim \triangle TMC$ by SSS~

D $\triangle ABC$ is not similar to $\triangle TMC$

EXAMPLE 4 Which of the following statements is true?

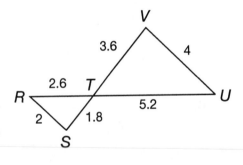

F $\triangle STR$ is similar to $\triangle VTU$ by AA

G $\triangle STR$ is similar to $\triangle VTU$ by SAS

H $\triangle STR$ is similar to $\triangle VTU$ by ASA

J $\triangle STR$ is not similar to $\triangle VTU$

Strategy

- Since you know of only one pair of congruent angles, $\angle RTS \cong \angle UTV$ (vertical angles), choices F and H can be eliminated.

- The ratio of the sides are $\frac{RT}{UT} = \frac{1}{2}$, $\frac{ST}{VT} = \frac{1}{2}$, and $\frac{RS}{UV} = \frac{1}{2}$. They are all equal. Therefore $\triangle STR$ is similar to $\triangle VTU$ by SAS.

Solution   Choose G.

(**NOTE**—You can also use SSS to prove these triangles congruent. Try It!)

75

Try It 4

In $\triangle PQR$, $\overline{PQ} = 8$, $\overline{QR} = 12$, and m$\angle Q = 40$. In $\triangle TUS$, $\overline{US} = 32$, $\overline{ST} = 50$ and m$\angle S = 40$. Which of the following statements is true?

F $\triangle PQR$ is similar to $\triangle TUS$ by AA

G $\triangle PQR$ is similar to $\triangle TUS$ by SAS

H $\triangle PQR$ is similar to $\triangle TUS$ by ASA

J $\triangle PQR$ is not similar to $\triangle TUS$

3 A line drawn parallel to one side of a triangle that intersects the other two sides divides those two sides proportionally:

$\overleftrightarrow{BE} \parallel \overleftrightarrow{CD}$ then $\dfrac{AB}{BC} = \dfrac{AE}{ED}$.

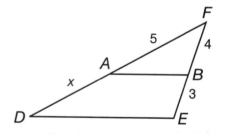

4 You can extended this relationship to the following: If you have three or more parallel lines cut by 2 transversals (here, the sides of the triangle), then the parallel lines divide the transversals proportionally.

$\overleftrightarrow{AB} \parallel \overleftrightarrow{CD} \parallel \overleftrightarrow{EF}$ then $\dfrac{AC}{CE} = \dfrac{BD}{DF}$

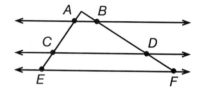

5 The **Angle Bisector Theorem** states that if a ray bisects an angle of a triangle, then it divides the opposite side into segments that are proportional to the adjacent sides of the angle. Given $\triangle ABD$ and $\overrightarrow{AC}$ bisects $\angle BAD$, then $\dfrac{BC}{CD} = \dfrac{AB}{AD}$.

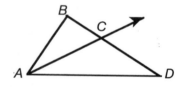

EXAMPLE 5 Given $\triangle DEF$ and $\overline{AB} \parallel \overline{DE}$, what is the value of x?

A $\dfrac{15}{4}$

B $\dfrac{20}{3}$

C $\dfrac{12}{5}$

D 4

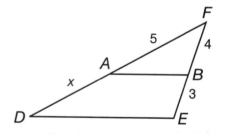

76

Strategy

- $\overleftrightarrow{AB}$ divides the sides of the triangle proportionally, so you need to set up the proportion and solve for x.

- $\dfrac{FA}{AD} = \dfrac{FB}{BE}$ Substitute values. $\rightarrow$ $\dfrac{5}{x} = \dfrac{4}{3}$

- Cross multiply. $\rightarrow$ $15 = 4x$

- Simplify by dividing by 4. $\rightarrow$ $\dfrac{15}{4} = x$

Solution Choose A.

Try It 5

Given the lengths shown and $\overleftrightarrow{BE} \parallel \overleftrightarrow{CD}$, what is the value for x?

A 4

B 9

C 11.5

D 12

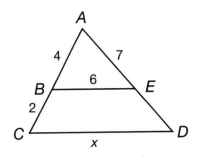

EXAMPLE 6 Given the lengths shown and $a \parallel b \parallel c \parallel d$ and $\overline{KP} = 24$, what is the value for x?

F 5

G 8

H 14

J 15

Strategy

- You know that the ratio of $\overline{KM} : \overline{MN} : \overline{NP}$ is equal to $5 : 2 : 8$.

- If each is multiplied by the same value, y, you get $5y : 2y : 8y$. Their sum is equal to 24. $24 = 5y + 2y + 8y$. Solve the equation.

- $24 = 15y \rightarrow \dfrac{24}{15} = y \rightarrow \dfrac{8}{5}$

- Therefore, $x = 5y = 5 \cdot \dfrac{8}{5} = 8$

Solution Choose G.

77

Try It 6

Given the lengths shown and
$a \parallel b \parallel c \parallel d$ and $\overrightarrow{SV} = 40$,
what is the value for $\overline{UV}$?

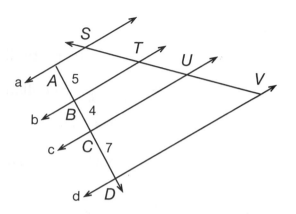

F 12.5

G 10

H 16

J 17.5

EXAMPLE 7 Given $\angle RVS \cong \angle SVT$ and the lengths of
the sides shown, what is the length of
$\overline{ST}$?

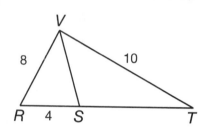

A   4

B   5

C   9

D 11

Strategy

- Since $\angle RVS \cong \angle SVT$, $\overrightarrow{VS}$ is an angle bisector of $\angle RVT$ and divides the side opposite it proportionally. $\frac{VR}{VT} = \frac{RS}{ST}$

- Substitute values in the proportion and solve. $\frac{8}{10} = \frac{4}{ST}$

- Cross multiply. $8(ST) = 40$

- Divide by 8. $ST = 5$

Solution   Choose B.

 Try It 7

Given $\angle BAD \cong \angle CAD$ and the lengths
of the sides shown, what is the length
of $\overline{DC}$, rounded to the nearest tenth?

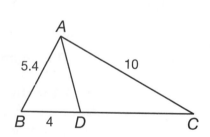

A   6

B   7

C   7.4

D 11.3

TRY IT Answers: *1. B*   *2. H*   *3. B*   *4. J*   *5. B*   *6. J*   *7. C*

78

1. The top of a yardstick 4 feet from an observer just lines up with the top of a tree 20 feet away. The right triangles *AED* and *ABC* are similar. What is the height of the tree?

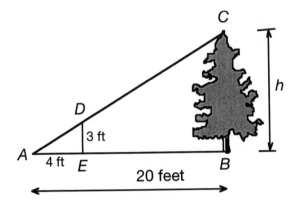

A 5
B 10
C 15
D 25

2. Which of the following statements *must* be true?

F If two polygons are similar they have the same shape.

G If two polygons are similar, they have the same size.

H All similar triangles are congruent.

J Any two cones are similar.

3. Given the figure below, by which reason is $\triangle PQT \sim \triangle PRS$?

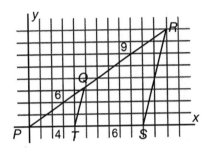

A AA
B ASA
C SAS
D not similar

4. $\triangle ABC \sim \triangle DEF$. Which of the following statements is false?

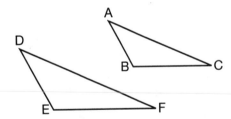

F $\dfrac{AB}{DE} = \dfrac{AC}{DF}$

G $\angle B \cong \angle E$

H $\dfrac{AB}{DE} = \dfrac{EF}{BC}$

J $\dfrac{AC}{BC} = \dfrac{DF}{EF}$

5. What is the scale factor for this pair of similar triangles? △ABC ~ △DBE

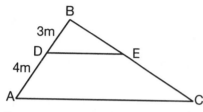

A $\frac{3}{4}$

B $\frac{3}{7}$

C $\frac{4}{3}$

D $\frac{4}{7}$

6. Given: ∠1 ≅ ∠2. Which of the following statements is used to prove $\frac{DC}{AC} = \frac{DE}{AB}$?

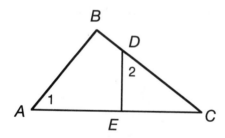

F △ABC ~ △EDC by SAS

G △ABC ~ △EDC by ASA

H △ABC ~ △DEC by AA

J △ABC ~ △DEC by ASA

7. Given ∠FEH ≅ ∠GEH and the lengths of the sides shown, what is the length of $\overline{FG}$?

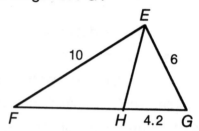

A 7

B 11.2

C 12

D 14.3

PYTHAGOREAN THEOREM

SOL G.7   *The student will solve practical problems involving right triangles **by using the Pythagorean Theorem and its converse**, properties of special right triangles, and right triangle trigonometry. Calculators will be used to solve problems and find decimal approximations for the solutions.*

REVIEW OF RIGHT TRIANGLES

1   In a right triangle, the side opposite the right angle is called the **hypotenuse**. In equations, it is usually represented by the letter c.

The other two sides are called the **legs**. In equations, they are usually represented by the letters a and b.

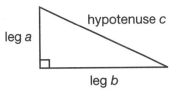

2   In any right triangle, there is a special relationship between the squares of the lengths of the legs and the square of the length of the hypotenuse. This relationship is called the **Pythagorean Theorem**. The Pythagorean Theorem states:

leg a^2 + leg b^2 = hypotenuse c^2. Or, more simply, $a^2 + b^2 = c^2$

EXAMPLE 1   Which measure represents the length of leg b in the triangle below?

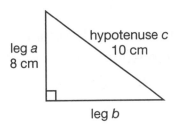

A   12.8
B   9
C   6
D   4.25

81

Strategy	• Use the Pythagorean Theorem.	$a^2 + b^2 = c^2$
	• Substitute:	$8^2 + b^2 = 10^2$
	• Simplify exponents:	$64 + b^2 = 100$
	• Simplify by subtracting 64 from both sides:.	$b^2 = 36$
	• Take the square root of each side:	$\sqrt{b^2} = \sqrt{36}$
		$b = 6$

Solution   Choose C.

Which measure represents the length of side $\overline{BC}$ in triangle *ABC*?

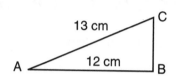

A 12.8

B 9

C 5

D 4.25

EXAMPLE 2 A rectangular swimming pool is 30 feet long and 16 feet wide. A life preserver at the side of the pool must have a rope attached, which must be at least the length of the pool's diagonal. Which of the following values represents the minimum length of the rope?

F 17

G 25

H 34

J 46

Strategy	• Use the Pythagorean Theorem:	$a^2 + b^2 = c^2$
	• Substitute the lengths of the legs:	$30^2 + 16^2 = c^2$
	• Simplify exponents:	$900 + 256 = c^2$
	• Simplify by addition:	$1156 = c^2$
	• Take the square root of each side:	$\sqrt{1156} = \sqrt{c^2} = 34$

Solution   Choose H.

Try It 2

Commuters can take a ferry from Bayside to Hampton. Which is the distance the ferry travels?

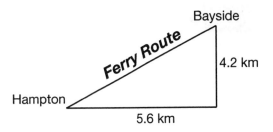

F   11.76 km
G   9.8 km
H   7.0 km
J   0.7 km

EXAMPLE 3 A 25-foot ladder is leaning against a building and the base of the ladder is 7 feet from the building. Which height does the ladder reach on the building?

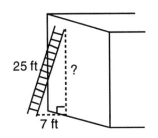

A 27 ft
B 24 ft
C 21 ft
D 18 ft

Strategy

- The leaning ladder is the hypotenuse of a right triangle, and so is the longest side. Since choice A is more than 25 ft, it cannot be a solution.

- Use the Pythagorean Theorem; $a^2 + b^2 = c^2$

- Substitute; $a^2 + 7^2 = 25^2$

- Simplify exponents; $a^2 + 49 = 625$

- Simplify by subtracting 49 from both sides; $a^2 = 576$

- Take the square root of each side; $\sqrt{a^2} = \sqrt{576}$

- $a = 24$.

Solution   Choose B.

Try It 3

Firefighters need to use a 60-foot ladder to save a child. She is 50 feet above street level. To the nearest tenth of a foot, how far from the bottom of the building must the ladder be placed in order to reach the child?

A   33.1 feet
B   33.2 feet
C   78.1 feet
D   78.0 feet

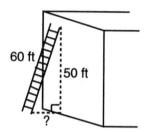

3 You can use the Pythagorean Theorem to develop the formula for finding the distance, d, between any two points A (x,y) and B (x_1,y_1) on a coordinate grid.

In the diagram on the right, point C (x_1,y) is used to create a right triangle with points A and B. The length of $\overline{AC}$ is $|x_1 - x|$ and the length of $\overline{BC}$ is $|y_1 - y|$.

Use the Pythagorean Theorem, $(x_1 - x)^2 + (y_1 - y)^2 = d^2$. Solve for d by taking the square root of both sides:

$d = \sqrt{(x_1 - x)^2 + (y_1 - y)^2}$. The result is the **distance formula..**

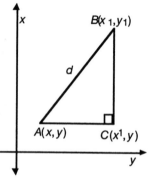

4 You can also use the Pythagorean Theorem to determine if a triangle is acute or obtuse, just by using the lengths of the sides.

- If the square of the longest side is **greater** than the sum of the squares of the other two sides (or simply, $c^2 > a^2 + b^2$), then the triangle is **obtuse**.

- If the square of the longest side is **less** than the sum of the squares of the other two sides (or simply, $c^2 < a^2 + b^2$), then the triangle is **acute**.

EXAMPLE 4 Which of the following values represent the distance $\overline{AB}$ in the diagram?

F   6
G   8
H   10
J   12

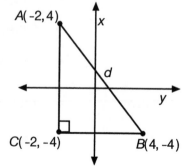

84

Strategy	• Since you are given ordered pairs, use the distance formula:

$$d = \sqrt{(x_1 - x)^2 + (y_1 - y)^2}$$

• Let (x,y) be $(-2,4)$ and (x_1,y_1) be $(4,-4)$

•	Substitute for x and y:	$\sqrt{(x_1 - -2)^2 + (y_1 - 4)^2}$
•	Substitute for x_1 and y_1:	$\sqrt{(4 - -2)^2 + (-4 - 4)^2}$
•	Simplify by adding:	$\sqrt{(6)^2 + (-8)^2}$
•	Simplify exponents:.	$\sqrt{36 + 64}$
•	Simplify by adding:	$\sqrt{100}$
•	Take the square root:	$\sqrt{100} = 10$

Solution   Choose H.

Try It 4

Which of the following values represents the length of $\overline{AC}$ to the nearest tenth of a unit?

F   2.2
G   5
H   3.6
J   13

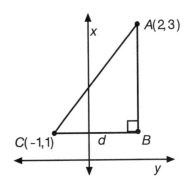

EXAMPLE 5 These are the measures of the sides of a triangle: (0.5, 1.2, 1.4) What type of triangle is formed?

A   acute
B   obtuse
C   right
D   isosceles

Strategy		
•	Use the Pythagorean Theorem.	$a^2 + b^2 = c^2$
•	Substitute.	$(0.5)^2 + (1.2)^2$ **?** $(1.4)^2$
•	Simplify exponents.	$.25 + 1.44$ **?** 1.96
•	Simplify by adding	$1.69 < 1.96$
•	Since the square of the longest side is greater than the sum of the squares of the other two sides, then the triangle is obtuse.	

Solution   Choose B.

Try It 5 These are the measures of the sides of a triangle. (0.5, 0.8, 0.9) What type of triangle is formed?

A   acute
B   obtuse
C   right
D   isosceles

EXAMPLE 6 Neil has placed stakes in the ground to mark the corners of the foundation of his new house. He calculates that the foundation is a parallelogram. Which of the following dimensions would make the foundation rectangular?

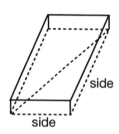

F   Sides: 20 ft and 46 ft; diagonal: 50 ft
G   Sides: 24 ft and 45 ft; diagonal: 52 ft
H   Sides: 26 ft and 48 ft; diagonal: 54 ft
J   Sides: 20 ft and 48 ft; diagonal: 52 ft

Strategy
- Use the Pythagorean Theorem: $a^2 + b^2 = c^2$
- Substitute the sides for a and b and the diagonal for c.
- Do this for each choice and simplify.

$$(20)^2 + (46)^2 \text{ ? } (50)^2 \rightarrow 400 + 2116 \text{ ? } 2500 \rightarrow 2516 \neq 2500$$

$$(24)^2 + (45)^2 \text{ ? } (52)^2 \rightarrow 576 + 2025 \text{ ? } 2704 \rightarrow 2601 \neq 2704$$

$$(26)^2 + (48)^2 \text{ ? } (54)^2 \rightarrow 676 + 2304 \text{ ? } 2916 \rightarrow 2980 \neq 2916$$

$$(20)^2 + (48)^2 \text{ ? } (52)^2 \rightarrow 400 + 2304 \text{ ? } 2704 \rightarrow 2704 = 2704$$

- Since choice J makes the Pythagorean Theorem true, it must form a right angle triangle, which makes the foundation rectangular.

Solution   Choose J.

86

Try It 6

Kate is building a gate for her fence. She is adding a length of wire to strengthen it. To the nearest tenth of a foot, what length of wire should she use to make sure the gate's corners are right angles?

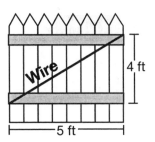

F 3.1

G 4.7

H 5.3

J 6.4

5 Several right triangles have integral sides—for example, a triangle with sides 3-4-5. Others are the 5-12-13 triangle and the 8-15-17 triangle. These and their multiples (like a 6-8-10 triangle, a multiple of a 3-4-5 triangle) are common on tests.

EXAMPLE 7 Vernon drives 26 miles to Bramwell from his home in Clark. He then drives 10 miles to De Paul. The diagram shows the relative positions of the three towns. How many miles must he drive to get home by the shortest route?

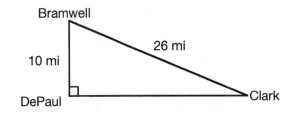

A 25

B 24

C 23

D 22.7

Strategy

- Try matching the two given distances with two sides of one of the triangles described in 5) above—or with multiples of these sides. They do not match.
- Try dividing the distances by their common factor 2. You get 5 and 13. These quotients match two of the sides of a **5**-12-**13** triangle.
- Multiply these measures times two: (5-**12**-13) x 2 = 10-**24**-26.

Solution   Choose B.

87

Try It 6 What is the length of the hypotenuse of a right triangle whose two legs measure 12 cm and 9 cm?

    F   21 cm
    G   17 cm
    H   15 cm
    J   13 cm

Try It Answers: *1. C   2. H   3. B   4. H   5. A   6. J   7. H*

Sample Virginia SOL Questions

1. Which measure represents the length of side $\overline{BC}$ in triangle ABC?

    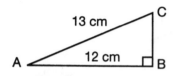

    A   12.8
    B   9
    C   5
    D   4.25

2. The lengths of the legs of a right triangle are 24 and 7. What is the length of its hypotenuse?

    F   7
    G   24
    H   25
    J   31

3. A flag company is making the flag shown below. What is the length of the stripe to the nearest tenth?

    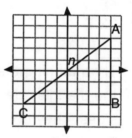

    A   10 m
    B   8.4 km
    C   7.2 m
    D   7.0 m

4. Which of the following values represents the distance *n*, to the nearest unit, in the diagram?

    F   9
    G   10
    H   11
    J   12

5. A building has a triangular roof. It is 36 feet across. At the center is a pole that is 24 feet long. What is the length of one slanting side of the roof?

A 26.8 ft
B 30 ft
C 36 ft
D 43.2 ft

6. Which of the following sets of sides of a triangle satisfy the Pythagorean Theorem?

F 4, 5, 7
G 8, 24, 25
H 20, 21, 29
J 5, 11, 13

SPECIAL RIGHT TRIANGLES

SOL G.7   *The student will solve practical problems involving right triangles by using the Pythagorean Theorem and its converse, **properties of special right triangles**, and right triangle trigonometry. Calculators will be used to solve problems and find decimal approximations for the solutions.*

There are two right triangles that have special relationships between the legs and the hypotenuse. Knowing the measure of one leg or of the hypotenuse allows you to find the measures of the others without using the Pythagorean Theorem. These triangles are named using the measures of their angles.

1 The first is a **45°–45°–90° triangle**. This is an **isosceles right triangle**, which means that both legs are the same length. If you know the length of a leg (a) of a 45°–45°–90° triangle, then the length of the hypotenuse is $a\sqrt{2}$ or a ratio of $a : a\sqrt{2}$.

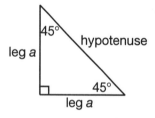

2 A **30°–60°–90° triangle** is the second special right triangle, and each side is a different length.

- If you know the length of the hypotenuse (h) of a 30°–60°–90° triangle, then the shorter leg is $\frac{1}{2}h$ and the longer leg is $\frac{1}{2}h\sqrt{3}$.

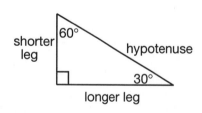
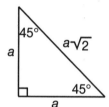

- If the length of the shorter leg (s) is known, then the length of the hypotenuse is **2s**, and the length of the longer leg is $s\sqrt{3}$. Another way to put this is in the form of a ratio of the lengths of the three sides, that is, $a : 2a : a\sqrt{3}$.

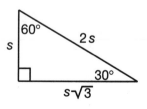

90

EXAMPLE 1 The area of a square is 169 cm^2. What is the length of the diagonal to the nearest tenth?

    A 13.0 cm

    B 18.4 cm

    C 19.5 cm

    D 20.2 cm

Strategy
- First find the square root of 169 to find the length of each side of the square: 13 cm

- The diagonal of the square divides it into 2 isosceles right triangles.

- You know the ratio of the length of a leg (**a**) of an isosceles (45°–45°–90°) right triangle to the length of the hypotenuse is **a** : **a**$\sqrt{2}$.

- The leg is 13, so the hypotenuse is 13$\sqrt{2}$ or 18.384776 ≈ 18.4

Solution   Choose B.

Try It 1

To the nearest tenth, what is the distance walked by taking path $\overline{AB}$ in the figure on the right?

    A   5.5

    B   7.7

    C 10.6

    D 11.8

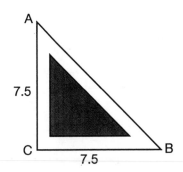

EXAMPLE 2 A slide carries hay bales from a barn loft 18 feet above the ground to ground level. The slide makes a 30° angle with the ground. What is the distance a hay bale travels on the slide?

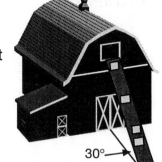

F 48 ft

G 36 ft

H $18\sqrt{3}$ ft

J 9 ft

Strategy
- You know that the leg opposite the 30° angle is the shorter leg, and that is 18 feet.

- Also, in a 30°–60°–90° triangle, if you know the length of the shorter (*s*) leg, then the length of the hypotenuse is **2s**.

- The shorter leg is 18 feet, and the hypotenuse is twice that, so it is 36 feet.

Solution   Choose G

Try It 2

To the nearest tenth of a centimeter, what is the length of the hypotenuse, *h*, of the triangle below?

F 40.7 cm

G 21.4 cm

H 20.7 cm

J   5.4 cm

10.7 cm   *h*   30°

EXAMPLE 3 Which of the following CANNOT be the lengths of a 30°–60°–90° triangle?

A $\frac{8}{3}, \frac{16}{3}, \frac{8}{3}\sqrt{3}$

B 6, 12, $6\sqrt{3}$

C 9, $\frac{9}{2}$, $9\sqrt{3}$

D 5, 10, $5\sqrt{3}$

Strategy	• The ratio of the sides of a 30°–60°–90° triangle is $a : 2a : a\sqrt{3}$.
	• Examine each choice and find the choice that is NOT in this ratio.
	• The second term should be twice the first. This occurs in choices A, B, and D but not C. Therefore choice C, CANNOT be a 30°–60°–90° triangle.

Solution	Choose C.

Try It 3

Which of the following CANNOT be the lengths of a 30°–60°–90° triangle?

A $\frac{2}{3}, \frac{4}{3}, \frac{2}{3}\sqrt{3}$

B 9, 18, 9√3

C $\frac{5}{2}, 5, \frac{5}{2}\sqrt{3}$

D 7, $\frac{7}{2}$, 7√3

EXAMPLE 4 A truck with a load of potatoes drives onto a 80-foot-long ramp at a potato chip factory. The front end of the ramp is raised 30° to empty the potatoes. To the nearest tenth of a foot, what is the height of the ramp?

F 30 ft
G 40 ft
H 69.3 ft
J 80 ft

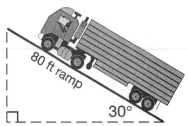

Strategy	• If you know the length of the hypotenuse (h) of a 30°–60°–90° triangle, then the shorter leg is $\frac{1}{2}h$.
	• The shorter leg of a 30°–60°–90° triangle is opposite the 30° angle.
	• So the height the ramp is raised is the shorter leg, or $\frac{1}{2}h$: 40 ft.

Solution	Choose G.

Try It 4 What is the length of the leg, *s*, opposite the 30°
angle in the figure on the right?

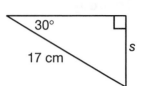

F   8.5 cm

G   15 cm

H   30 cm

J   34 cm

EXAMPLE 5 A 26-ft. ladder leans against a barn. The angle it makes with the
ground is 60°. To the nearest tenth of a foot, how far up the side of
the barn does the ladder reach?

A   13.0 ft.

B   18.4 ft.

C   22.5 ft.

D   22.6 ft.

Strategy

•   The triangle that is formed is a 30°–60°–90° triangle, and the side
opposite the 60° angle is the longer leg. The hypotenuse is the
26-ft ladder.

•   The ratio of the longer leg to the hypotenuse is $a\sqrt{3} : 2a$. You set
up a proportion to solve this problem. $\dfrac{a\sqrt{3}}{2a} = \dfrac{\text{longer leg}}{26}$

Cross multiply: $26a \cdot \sqrt{3} = 2a \cdot \text{longer leg}$

Divide both sides by 2*a*: $\dfrac{26a \cdot \sqrt{3}}{2a} = \dfrac{2a \cdot \text{longer leg}}{2a}$

Simplify: $13\sqrt{3} = \text{longer leg}$

Evaluate, using a calculator: $13\sqrt{3} \approx 22.516$

To the nearest tenth, the ladder reaches 22.5 feet.

Solution   Choose C.

What is the altitude or height, to the nearest tenth of a centimeter, of the equilateral triangle on the right?

A   6.0 cm

B   10.4 cm

C   17.0 cm

D   20.8 cm

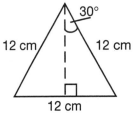

EXAMPLE 6 The shorter leg of a 30°–60°–90° triangle is 3.4 cm long. What is the perimeter of the triangle to the nearest tenth of a centimeter?

F   13.6 cm

G   13.9 cm

H   16.0 cm

J   16.1 cm

Strategy

• To find the perimeter you add the lengths of each side of the triangle. The ratio of the lengths of the sides of a 30°–60°–90° triangle is $a : 2a : a\sqrt{3}$.

Substitute 3.4 for a :	$3.4 + 2(3.4) + 3.4\sqrt{3}$
Simplify by multiplying:	$3.4 + 6.8 + 5.888973$
Simplify by adding:	16.088973

To the nearest tenth of a centimeter, the perimeter is 16.1 cm.

Solution   Choose J.

Try It 6

The shorter leg of a 30°–60°–90° triangle is 4.4 cm long. What is the perimeter of the triangle to the nearest tenth of a centimeter?

F   17.6 cm

G   19.4 cm

H   20.8 cm

J   20.9 cm

95

EXAMPLE 7 The blades of a windmill are the same length and intersect at right angles. The distance between the outer tips of two consecutive blades is 36 feet. To the nearest tenth of a foot, what is the length of each blade?

36 ft

A 50.9 ft
B 25.5 ft
C 20.8 ft
D 18.0 ft

Strategy

- The distances between the four blade tips form a square. The blades form the legs of four 45°–45°–90° triangles.

- The length of a leg of these triangle is $\frac{1}{2}h\sqrt{2}$. You already know the length of h: 36 ft.

- Substitute 36 for h in $\frac{1}{2}h\sqrt{2}$. and simplify the expression.

$$\frac{1}{2} \cdot 36 \cdot \sqrt{2} \to 18 \cdot \sqrt{2} \approx 25.5.$$

Solution   Choose B.

 Try It 7

The blades of a four-blade ceiling fan are the same length and intersect at right angles. The distance between the outer tips of two consecutive blades is 60 inches. To the nearest hundredth of an inch, what is the length of each blade?

A 84.85 in.
B 51.96 in.
C 42.43 in.
D 30.00 in.

TRY IT Answers: *1. C   2. G   3. D   4. F   5. B   6. H   7. C*

1. Which of the following CANNOT be the lengths of a 30°–60°–90° triangle?

   A $\frac{4}{3}$, $\frac{8}{3}$, $\frac{4}{3}\sqrt{3}$

   B $\frac{8}{2}$, 8, $\frac{8}{2}\sqrt{3}$

   C 7, 14, $7\sqrt{3}$

   D 3, $\frac{3}{2}$, $3\sqrt{3}$

2. The leg opposite the 30° angle of a 30°–60°–90° triangle is 1.25 m long. To the nearest hundredth of a meter, what is the perimeter of the triangle?

   F 4.83 m
   G 5.29 m
   H 5.92 m
   J 6.83 m

3. To the nearest tenth of a meter, what is the length of the hypotenuse of the triangle below?

   A 40.1 m
   B 23.2 m
   C 20.1 m
   D 5.8 m

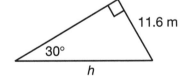

4. What is the altitude or height, to the nearest tenth of a centimeter, of the equilateral triangle below?

   F 4.0 cm
   G 5.7 cm
   H 6.9 cm
   J 7.2 cm

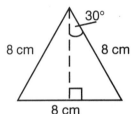

5. To the nearest hundredth of a meter, what is the length of the leg, s, opposite the 60° angle in the figure below?

   A 20.78
   B 16.97
   C 10.39
   D 6

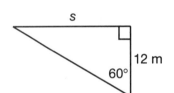

6. Two sports cars leave the same parking lot at 9 a.m. One heads due south, the other car travels east, both are traveling at the same speed. After one hour they are 63.6 miles apart. Which represents the distance each car has traveled?

   F 55 miles
   G 50 miles
   H 45 miles
   J 40 miles

RIGHT TRIANGLE TRIGONOMETRY

SOL G.7   *The student will solve practical problems involving right triangles by using the Pythagorean Theorem and its converse, properties of special right triangles, and **right triangle trigonometry**. Calculators will be used to solve problems and find decimal approximations for the solutions.*

Trigonometric ratios are the ratios of the length of two sides of a **right triangle**. There are three important trigonometric ratios associated with right triangles. They are the *sine ratio, cosine ratio*, and the *tangent ratio*. Every angle has a unique sine, cosine, and tangent ratio associated with it.

1 The **sine ratio** of an acute angle A, or sine A, is the ratio between the length of the **side opposite** $\angle A$ and the length of the **hypotenuse**. The abbreviation of sine is **sin**.

- $\sin A = \dfrac{\text{the length of the side opposite } \angle A}{\text{the length of the hypotenuse}}$

2 The **cosine ratio** of an acute angle A, or cosine A, is the ratio between the length of the **side adjacent** to $\angle A$ and the length of the **hypotenuse**. The abbreviation of cosine is **cos**.

- $\cos A = \dfrac{\text{the length of the side adjacent to } \angle A}{\text{the length of the hypotenuse}}$

3 The **tangent ratio** of an acute angle A, or **tangent A**, is the ratio between the length of the **side opposite** $\angle A$ and the length of the **side adjacent** to $\angle A$. The abbreviation of tangent is **tan**. The product of the tangent of complementary angles is always one.

- $\tan A = \dfrac{\text{the length of the side opposite } \angle A}{\text{the length of the side adjacent to } \angle A}$

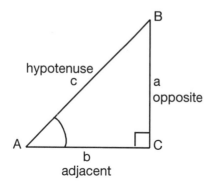
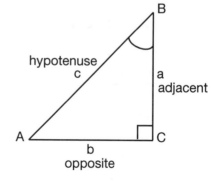

98

4 Sine $A = \frac{a}{c}$ is the same as the cosine of the other acute angle $B = \frac{a}{c}$.

5 Similarly, cosine $A = \frac{b}{c}$ is the same as sine $B = \frac{b}{c}$.

6 Tangent A ($\frac{a}{b}$) is the **reciprocal** of tangent B ($\frac{b}{a}$).

Each ratio is written in either a fractional or decimal form. Many ratios, when written as decimals, are rounded to a particular decimal place value, and the symbol $\approx$ is used to mean "approximately equal."

EXAMPLE 1 Tyrone made a sketch after taking several measures from a river bank. Use the sketch on the right. What is the width of the river, x, to the nearest ten feet?

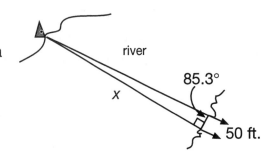

A   10 ft
B   50 ft
C   600 ft
D   610 ft

Strategy   • When you need to find a length of a leg and you have the length of the other leg, you use the tangent ratio.

$$\textbf{tan } A = \frac{\text{the length of the side opposite } \angle A}{\text{the length of the side adjacent to } \angle A}$$

• Substitute your known values. $\tan 85.3° = \frac{x}{50}$

• Cross multiply $x = 50 \cdot \tan 85.3°$

• Use your calculator to simplify.   50 $\boxed{\text{X}}$ $\boxed{\text{TAN}}$ 85.3 $\boxed{\text{EXE}}$

• The value you see is 608.1617... $\approx$ 608, which rounds to 610.

Solution   Choose D.

Try It 1 ➤

A tree 36 feet tall casts a shadow which forms an angle of 50° with the ground. What is the length of the shadow to the nearest tenth of a foot?

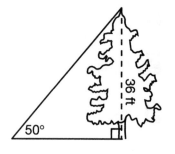

A 30.2 ft

B 42.9 ft

C 46.9 ft

D 68.8 ft

7 When you look up to a figure above you, or on a tower, the angle formed by the horizontal and your line of sight is called the **angle of elevation**. On the other hand, when you look down at a figure, the angle formed by the horizontal and your line of sight is called the **angle of depression.**

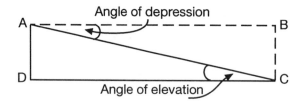

EXAMPLE 2 A lookout spots a fire from a 39 m-tall tower. The angle of depression from the fire spotter to the fire is 14°. To the nearest meter, what is the distance to the fire from the base of the tower?

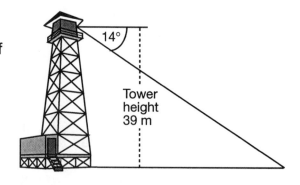

F   19 m

G   62 m

H   156 m

J   161 m

100

Strategy
- There are two ways to solve this problem using the tangent ratio.

$$\tan A = \frac{\text{the length of the side opposite } \angle A}{\text{the length of the side adjacent to } \angle A}$$

One is to use the angle of 14° and 39 m as the opposite side. The other is to use as the angle the complement of 14° or 90 − 14 = 76° and 39 m as the adjacent side.

- Substitute your known values. $\tan 14° = \frac{39}{x}$

  Cross multiply: $x \cdot \tan 14° = 39$

  Use your calculator to simplify: 39 $\boxed{\div}$ $\boxed{\text{TAN}}$ 14 $\boxed{\text{EXE}}$

The value you see is 156.4204... ≈ 156.4, which rounds to 156.

- Substitute your known values: $\tan 76° = \frac{x}{39}$

  Cross multiply: $x = 39 \cdot \tan 76°$

  Use your calculator to simplify: 39 $\boxed{\text{X}}$ $\boxed{\text{TAN}}$ 76 $\boxed{\text{EXE}}$

The value you see is 156.4204... ≈ 156.4 which rounds to 156.

Solution   Choose H.

 Try It 2

A lookout spots a fire from a 42 m-tall tower. The angle of depression from the fire spotter to the fire is 13°. To the nearest meter, what is the distance to the fire from the base of the tower?

F   187 m
G   182 m
H   69 m
J   56 m

EXAMPLE 3 Katherine is flying a kite with 300 ft of kite string out. The string makes an angle of 56° with the level ground. To the nearest tenth of a foot, how high is her kite?

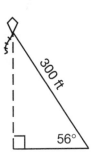

A   167.7 ft
B   248.7 ft
C   361.8 ft
D   444.7 ft

Strategy
- You are given a hypotenuse, so you will either use sine or cosine.
- Since you need to find the side opposite the angle, you will use the sine ratio: $\sin A = \dfrac{\text{the length of the side opposite } \angle A}{\text{the length of the hypotenuse}}$
- Substitute your known values: $\sin 56° = \dfrac{x}{300}$

Cross multiply: $x = 300 \cdot \sin 56°$

Use your calculator to simplify: $300 \boxed{X} \boxed{SIN} 56 \boxed{EXE}$

The value you see is $248.7112... \approx 248.7$.

Solution   Choose B.

 A slide 4.2 meters long makes a 35° angle with the ground. How high above the ground is the top of the slide?

A 5.1

B 3.4

C 2.9

D 2.4

8 If you know the trigonometric ratio of an angle, you can find the measure of the angle by using a scientific or graphing calculator.

- If the **sine** of $\angle A \approx .54464$, then to find the measure of $\angle A$, press the reciprocal of sine $\boxed{\text{SIN}^{-1}}$ key and enter .54464. The result should be 33.00006593, which is approximately 33°, so the measure of $\angle A \approx 33°$.

- If the **cosine** of $\angle B \approx .54464$, then to find the measure of $\angle B$, press the reciprocal of cosine $\boxed{\text{COS}^{-1}}$ key and enter .54464. The result should be 56.99993407, which is approximately 57°, so the measure of $\angle B \approx 57°$.

- If the **tangent** of $\angle A \approx .64941$, then to find the measure of $\angle$, press the reciprocal of tangent $\boxed{\text{TAN}^{-1}}$ key and enter .64941. The result should be 33.00009699, which is approximately 33°, so the measure of $\angle A \approx 33°$.

EXAMPLE 4 The Leaning Tower of Pisa (right) measures 55 m from base to top (the hypotenuse in the diagram at right). At what angle from the vertical does the Tower lean? Round your answer to the nearest tenth of a degree.

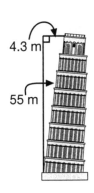

F 85. 5°

G 83.3°

H   6.7°

J   4.5°

Strategy

- Use the sine ratio, because you need to find the angle at the base of the tower. $\text{sine} = \dfrac{\text{opposite}}{\text{hypotenuse}} = \dfrac{4.3}{55}$

- Since the question asks you to find an angle, you will use the inverse function of the sine ratio on your calculator to find the measure of the angle.

- Enter this key sequence: $\boxed{\text{SIN}^{-1}}\ \dfrac{4.3}{55}\ \boxed{\text{EXE}} \approx 4.484064216$

- This rounds to 4.5°.

Solution   Choose J.

Try It 4

What is the measure of angle *x* in the figure below to the nearest tenth of a degree?

F 58.0°

G 51.3°

H 38.7°

J 32.0°

EXAMPLE 5 The sun shines on a 25-foot tree so that it casts a shadow 18 feet long. To the nearest degree, what angle do the sun rays make with the ground?

A   54°

B   46°

C   44°

D   35°

25 ft

18 ft

103

Strategy

- You have the measures of two legs of a right triangle, so you can find the tangent ratio. You use the angle on the ground as your reference angle to set up the ratio. $\dfrac{\text{opposite}}{\text{adjacent}} = \dfrac{25}{18}$

- Since the question asks you to find an angle, you will use the inverse function of the tangent ratio on your calculator to find the measure of the angle.

- Enter this key sequence: $\boxed{\text{TAN}^{-1}} \dfrac{25}{18} \boxed{\text{EXE}} \approx 54.24611275$

Solution Choose A.

Try It 5

What is the measure of angle x in the figure on the right to the nearest tenth of a degree?

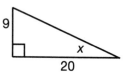

A 24.2°

B 26.7°

C 63.3°

D 65.8°

EXAMPLE 6 Use the diagram on the right. What is the cosine of x as a fraction in simplest form?

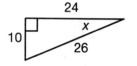

F $\dfrac{5}{12}$

G $\dfrac{5}{13}$

H $\dfrac{12}{13}$

J $2\dfrac{2}{5}$

Strategy

- Remember, cosine is $\dfrac{\text{adjacent}}{\text{hypotenuse}}$. The hypotenuse is 26, and the adjacent side to angle x is 24. So the cos $= \dfrac{24}{26}$.

- Now all you have to do is simplify the fraction by factoring out all the common factors. In this case, the common factor is 2.
$$\frac{2 \cdot 12}{2 \cdot 13} = \frac{12}{13}$$

Solution Choose H.

Try It 6 Use the diagram on the right. What is the sine of x as a fraction in simplest form?

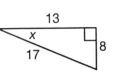

F $1\frac{7}{8}$

G $\frac{15}{17}$

H $\frac{8}{15}$

J $\frac{8}{17}$

EXAMPLE 7 Zack wants to find the distance across a pond. He climbs a 30-ft. observation tower. At the top, he sights along two sides of a carpenter's square, locating points B and C. He determines C is 5 feet from A. What is the distance across the pond?

A 180 ft

B 185 ft

C 190 ft

D 195 ft

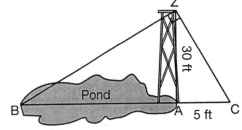

Strategy

• You have the lengths of two legs of $\triangle ACZ$, so by using the inverse function of the tangent ratio on your calculator you find the measure of $\angle C$. Tan $\angle C = \frac{30}{5} = 6$. $\boxed{\text{TAN}^{-1}}$ $6 \approx 80.5376°$

• Use the cosine to find the hypotenuse of $\triangle ACZ$, which is the leg of the larger triangle, $\triangle BCZ$. $\text{Cos} \angle C = \frac{\text{adjacent}}{\text{hypotenuse}}$

Substitute values. $\text{Cos } 80.5376 = \frac{5}{\text{hypotenuse}}$

Simplify. $\text{Hypotenuse} = \frac{5}{\text{Cos } 80.5376} \approx 30.4138$

• Now you have an angle and a leg of the $\triangle BCZ$, larger triangle, so you can find the hypotenuse $\overline{BC}$ by using the cosine ratio.

Substitute values. $\text{Cos } 80.5376 = \frac{30.4138}{\text{hypotenuse}}$

Simplify. $\text{Hypotenuse} = \frac{30.4138}{\text{Cos } 80.5376} \approx 184.99998$

105

- Subtract the 5 ft from the length of the hypotenuse of △BCZ, and you have the distance across the pond, 180 feet.

Solution   Choose A.

Try It 7 ▶

What is the measure of *h* in the figure on the right to the nearest tenth?

A 1.6
B 3.3
C 4.1
D 5.7

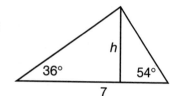

TRY IT Answers: **1. A   2. G   3. D   4. H   5. A   6. J   7. B**

Sample Virginia SOL Questions

1. A line from the top of a 20-ft tree to the "top" of its shadow forms an angle of 40° with the ground. What is the length of the shadow, to the nearest hundredth of a foot?

   A 23.84 ft
   B 21.45 ft
   C 21.27 ft
   D 18.00 ft

2. In the figure below, what is the length of *x*, to the nearest hundredth?

   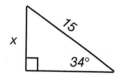

   F   8.39
   G 10.12
   H 12.44
   J 22.24

3. In the figure below what is the tan of angle *A* as a fraction in simplest form ?

   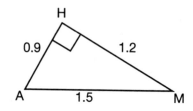

   A $\frac{3}{4}$

   B $\frac{4}{5}$

   C $\frac{4}{3}$

   D $\frac{5}{4}$

106

4. A paraskier is being towed behind a boat on 85 yards of rope. The angle of elevation is 35°. To the nearest tenth, what is the height of the paraskier from the surface of the water?

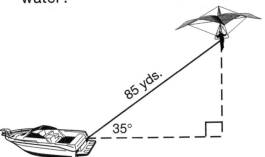

F   143.4 ft

G   175.1 ft

H   204.8 ft

J   357.0 ft

5. In the figure below, what is the measure of angle *x* to the nearest hundredth of a degree?

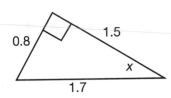

A   28.07°

B   30.28°

C   54.92°

D   61.93°

6. The angle of elevation from a ship to the top of a 200-foot-high lighthouse on the shore is 18°. To the nearest foot, how far is the ship from the shore?

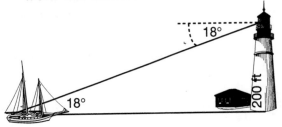

F   65 ft

G   210 ft

H   616 ft

J   647 ft

QUADRILATERALS

SOL G.8   *The student will*
- *investigate and identify properties of quadrilaterals involving opposite sides and angles, consecutive sides and angles, and diagonals.*
- *prove these properties of quadrilaterals using algebraic and coordinate as well as deductive proofs.*
- *use properties of quadrilaterals to solve practical problems.*

1 **Quadrilaterals** are polygons with four sides.

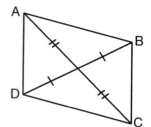

- A quadrilateral with 2 pairs of opposite sides parallel and congruent is a **parallelogram**.

  - The diagonals (line segments that connect 2 vertices that are not next to each other) of a parallelogram bisect each other.

  - The opposite angles are congruent. $\angle A \cong \angle C$

  - Consecutive angles (those that share a common side) are supplementary. $m\angle A + m\angle B = 180°$

2 Parallelograms with additional specific properties have special names:

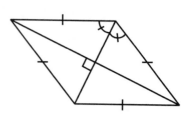

- **Rhombus** (*plural,* **rhombi**)—a parallelogram with four congruent sides. Diagonals are perpendicular, bisect each other, and bisect opposite angles.

- **Rectangle**—a parallelogram with four right angles. The diagonals are congruent and bisect each other.

- **Square**—a parallelogram with four right angles and four congruent sides. The diagonals are congruent, perpendicular, and bisect each other

3 Other quadrilaterals with additional specific properties also have special names:

- A **trapezoid** is a quadrilateral with only one pair of parallel sides. The midsegment is a line segment parallel to the bases, midway between them, and $\frac{1}{2}$ the length of the sum of the bases.

- An **isosceles trapezoid** has base angles that are congruent and diagonals that are congruent. $\overline{AD} \cong \overline{BC}$

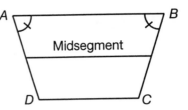

- A **kite** has two pairs of adjacent congruent sides. The diagonals are perpendicular. One of the diagonals bisects the angles at its endpoints. It also bisects the other diagonal.

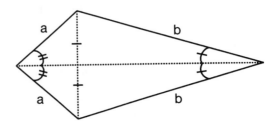

EXAMPLE 1 Which set of information determines that a quadrilateral is a square?

    A The diagonals are perpendicular but not congruent.

    B The diagonals are congruent and perpendicular.

    C The diagonals are perpendicular and neither bisects the other.

    D The diagonals are congruent but not perpendicular.

Strategy
- You know that a quadrilateral is a square if its diagonals are perpendicular, congruent, and bisect each other.
- Only choice B states two of these factors.

Solution   Choose B.

Which set of information determines that a quadrilateral is a kite?

    A The diagonals are not congruent and not perpendicular.

    B The diagonals are perpendicular and neither bisects each other.

    C The diagonals are congruent but not perpendicular.

    D The diagonals are perpendicular and one bisects the other.

EXAMPLE 2 Which of the following is a FALSE statement?

F All squares are rectangles.
G All trapezoids are polygons.
H All rectangles are quadrilaterals.
J All rhombi are squares.

Strategy

• Start with the properties of the second figure and determine if the first figure has all of the defining properties of the second. If it does, then it is a true statement.

— Choice **F**: A rectangle is a parallelogram with four right angles, and the diagonals are congruent. A square has these properties, so the statement is true.

— Choice **G**: A polygon is a closed figure. A trapezoid is a closed figure. This is a true statement.

— Choice **H**: A quadrilateral is a polygon with four sides. A rectangle is a polygon with four sides. This is a true statement.

— Choice **J**: A square has diagonals that are congruent. Since the diagonals of a rhombus do not have to be congruent, the statement is false.

Solution Choose J.

 Try It 2

Which of the following is impossible to draw?

F A rectangle that is not a trapezoid.
G A rectangle that is not a parallelogram.
H A rectangle that is not a rhombus.
J A rectangle that is not a square.

110

EXAMPLE 3 Given □*ABCD* is a rhombus, m∠*DCA* = 30°
and $\overline{EB}$ = 17. What is the length of $\overline{CB}$?

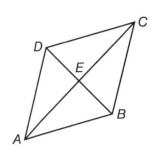

    A 17

    B 29.4

    C 34

    D 47

Strategy

- The diagonal of a rhombus bisects the angles at its endpoints, so ∠*DCA* ≅ ∠*BCA* and Δ*EBC* is a 30°–60°–90° right triangle.

- You know the side opposite the 30° angle, $\overline{EB}$, is $\frac{1}{2}$ the length of the hypotenuse, $\overline{CB}$.

- $\overline{EB}$ = 17, so double 17 to find the length of $\overline{CB}$ → 34.

Solution   Choose C.

Given □*ABCD* is a rhombus, m∠*DBA* = 60°
and $\overline{EB}$ = 16. What is the length of $\overline{DC}$?

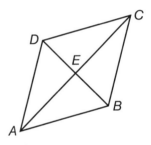

    A 76

    B 55.4

    C 32

    D 27.7

EXAMPLE 4 Given □*ABCD* is isosceles, $\overline{AB}$ = 18*y* – 2,
$\overline{BC}$ = 2*y* + 7, and $\overline{CD}$ = 6*y* + 4. What is the
length of $\overline{DA}$?

    F   5

    G   7

    H   8

    J   11

Strategy

- Since □*ABCD* is isosceles, you know that the non-parallel legs are congruent. Set them equal to themselves and solve for *y*, then substitute for *y* in 2*y* + 7 to find the length of $\overline{BC}$.

111

- $18y - 2 = 6y + 4$

  Simplify by adding 2 to both sides: $18y = 6y + 6$

  Subtract $6y$: $12y = 6$

  Divide by 12: $y = \frac{1}{2}$

- Substitute $\frac{1}{2}$ for y in $2y + 7 \rightarrow 2(\frac{1}{2}) + 7 \rightarrow 1 + 7 \rightarrow 8$. The length of $\overline{BC}$ is 8.

Solution   Choose H.

 Try It 4

In isosceles $\triangle JKLM$, leg $JK = 7x - 3$, base $KL = 3x - 6$, and leg $LM = 5x + 5$. What is the length of $\overline{KL}$?

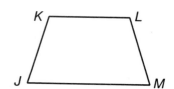

F   4

G   6

H   8

J   12

EXAMPLE 5 In the diagram on the right, $\square ABCD$ is a rhombus. What is the measure of $\angle 1$?

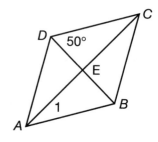

A   90°

B   50°

C   40°

D   30°

Strategy

- The diagonals of a rhombus are perpendicular, so that $\angle BEA$ is 90°. The opposite sides of a rhombus are ∥ and $\overline{DB}$ is a transversal, making $\angle CDB$ and $\angle ABD$ congruent because they are alternate interior angles.

- m$\angle ABD$ is 50°. $\triangle ABE$ is a right triangle. Because the acute angles of a right triangle are complementary, m$\angle 1$ is 40°.

Solution   Choose B.

Try It 5

In the diagram on the right, ☐*STUV* is a rectangle. What is the measure of ∠1?

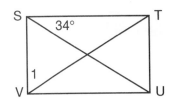

A 34°

B 56°

C 68°

D 112°

EXAMPLE 6 Kate has to prove that the surface of the ironing board, on the right, is parallel to the floor. She knows $\overline{MX} \cong \overline{PX}$ and $\overline{NX} \cong \overline{QX}$. Which of the following is a good reason for stating that quadrilateral *MNPQ* is a parallelogram?

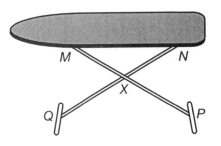

F Opposite sides are congruent.

G Opposite angles are congruent.

H Consecutive angles are supplementary.

J Diagonals of a parallelogram bisect each other.

Strategy
- You know that $\overline{MX} \cong \overline{PX}$ and $\overline{NX} \cong \overline{QX}$ are diagonals of quadrilateral *MNPQ*. This means that $\overline{MP}$ and $\overline{NQ}$ bisect each other.

- You know that the diagonals of a parallelogram bisect each other.

Solution Choose J.

113

Try It 6

Grady knows the following about the railroad bridge pictured below: $\overline{ED} \parallel \overline{BC}$ and $\overline{AB} \parallel \overline{EF}$. He needs to prove $\overline{EQ} \cong \overline{QB}$. Which of the following could be his reason for stating that quadrilateral *ERBP* is a parallelogram?

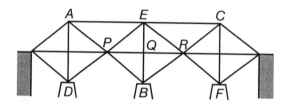

F Opposite sides are parallel.

G Opposite angles are congruent.

H Consecutive angles are supplementary.

J Diagonals of a parallelogram bisect each other.

TRY IT Answers: **1. D** **2. G** **3. C** **4. G** **5. B** **6. F**

Sample Virginia SOL Questions

1. Which of the following is NOT true of parallelograms?

    A The opposite sides are congruent.

    B The opposite angles are congruent.

    C Consecutive angles are complementary.

    D The diagonals bisect each other.

2. In an isosceles trapezoid *JKLM*, leg $\overline{JK} = 7x - 3$, base $\overline{KL} = 9x - 5$, and leg $\overline{LM} = 5x + 3$. What is the length of $\overline{KL}$?

    F 18

    G 22

    H 27

    J 157

3. Given ▱*ABCD* is a rhombus, $\overline{AB}$ = 18 and $\overline{BD}$ = 20. To the nearest tenth, what is the length of $\overline{AC}$?

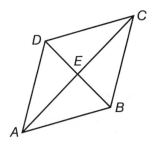

A   15.0
B   25.5
C   29.9
D   34.6

4. A quadrilateral has one of the following properties. Which MUST it have to be parallelogram?

F   two adjacent angles equal
G   one pair of adjacent sides equal
H   two pairs of parallel sides
J   a diagonal as axis of symmetry

5. Which of the following pairs of conditions is NOT sufficient to prove that quadrilateral *FGHJ* is a parallelogram?

    I. $\overline{FG} \parallel \overline{HJ}$
    II. $\overline{FG} \cong \overline{HJ}$
    III. $\overline{FJ} \cong \overline{GH}$
    IV. ∠*F* is supplementary to ∠*G*

A   **I** and **II**
B   **I** and **III**
C   **II** and **III**
D   **III** and **IV**

6. In the diagram below, ▱*FGHJ* is a rectangle. What is the measure of ∠1?

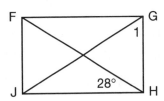

F   28°
G   56°
H   62°
J   124°

115

INTERIOR & EXTERIOR ANGLES

SOL G.9 *The student will use measures of interior and exterior angles of polygons to solve problems. Tessellations and tiling problems will be used to make connections to art, construction, and nature.*

1 A **polygon** is a simple closed figure formed by 3 or more points joined by line segments. The points where the line segments meet are called **vertices**.

2 To find the sum of the **interior angles** of a polygon, divide it into triangles (You know that the sum of the **interior angles** of a triangle is 180°.) Simply draw all the possible diagonals from one vertex, count the number of triangles formed, and multiply by 180°.

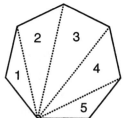

- Look at the heptagon (7-sides) on the right. There are 5 triangles formed by all the possible diagonals that can be drawn from one vertex: 5 • 180° = 900°. The sum of the angles of a heptagon is 900°.

- Another way to find the sum of the interior angles is to use the formula (*n* - 2) • 180°, where *n* is the number of sides of the polygon. For the heptagon: (7 - 2) • 180° = 5 • 180° = 900°.

3 A **regular polygon** is one with all sides congruent (**equilateral**) and all angles congruent (**equiangular**).

- To find the measure of one of the interior angles of a regular polygon, you use the following ratio:

$$\frac{\text{sum of the interior angles of the polygon}}{\text{the number of sides of the polygon}} = \frac{(n - 2) \cdot 180°}{n}$$

Thus, to find the measure of the interior angle of a regular heptagon, you substitute and simplify.

$$\frac{(7 - 2) \cdot 180°}{7} = \frac{900°}{7} \approx 128.57°.$$

116

4 An **exterior angle** of a polygon is an angle formed by one side and a ray extending out from an adjacent side.

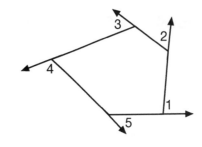

- The sum of the exterior angles of a polygon is always 360°, no matter how many sides the polygon has.
- The measure of each exterior angle of a regular polygon of n sides is $\frac{360°}{n}$.

EXAMPLE 1 Henry is making a sign in the shape of a regular pentagon. What is the measure of each interior angle of the sign?

    A 72°

    B 96°

    C 108°

    D 120°

Strategy
- To find the measure of each interior angle of a polygon, use the formula: $\frac{(n-2) \cdot 180°}{n}$
- A pentagon has 5 sides, so substitute 5 for n in the formula and simplify:

$$\frac{(n-2) \cdot 180°}{n} \rightarrow \frac{(5-2) \cdot 180°}{5} \rightarrow \frac{(3) \cdot 180°}{5} \rightarrow \frac{540°}{5} \rightarrow 108°$$

Solution Choose C.

Try It 1 Diane is making a clock in the shape of a regular octagon from 8 pieces of wood. What is the measure of the angle between 2 of the pieces of wood?

    A 240°

    B 135°

    C 120°

    D 45°

EXAMPLE 2 What is the measure of angle x?

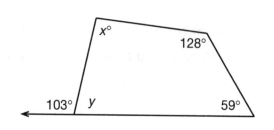

F 77°

G 86°

H 90°

J 96°

Strategy
- First find the measure of ∠y. Because ∠y and 103° form a straight angle (180°), you can find the measure of ∠y by subtracting. 180° − 103° = 77°

- You know the sum of the interior angles of a quadrilateral is 360°. By subtracting the 3 known angles from 360° you can find the measure of x.
  360° − (59° + 128° + 77°) = 360° − 264° = 96°

Solution   Choose J.

Try It 2

What is the measure of angle x?

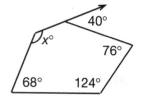

F 105°

G 140°

H 132°

J   92°

EXAMPLE 3 What is the measure of an exterior angle of a regular 12-sided polygon?

A   30°

B   40°

C 120°

D 150°

Strategy
- The sum of the exterior angles of any polygon is always 360°. To find the measure of an exterior angle of a regular polygon, divide 360° by the number of sides of the polygon.

- 360° ÷ 12 = 30°

Solution   Choose A.

118

Try It 3

What is the measure of an exterior angle of a regular 15-sided polygon?

A 15°

B 24°

C 28°

D 30°

EXAMPLE 4 The line ℓ is a line of symmetry for figure *ABCDE*. What is the measure of $\angle ABC$?

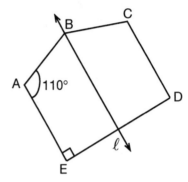

F 70°

G 110°

H 140°

J 160°

Strategy

- This is a 5-sided figure, and the sum of the interior angles is 540°.

- The line ℓ divides the figure into two congruent mirror images. So you know that $\angle E \cong \angle D = 90°$ and $\angle A \cong \angle C = 110°$.

- The sum of these 4 angles is 90 + 90 + 110 + 110 = 400°.

- $m\angle ABC = 540° - 400° = 140°$.

Solution   Choose H.

Try It 4

The line ℓ is a line of symmetry for figure *MNOPQ*. What is the measure of $\angle MNO$?

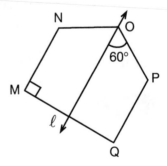

F 60°

G 70°

H 120°

J 140°

119

5 Certain arrangements of polygons will **tesselate** or **tile a plane** (*Tiling a plane* means *completely* covering the plane with polygons—with no overlapping and no spaces between the polygons.) For regular polygons to tile a plane, the sum of one interior angle from each of the figures must be 360°. If the sum is less than 360°, then there will be gaps between the figures. If the sum is greater than 360°, the figures will overlap. For examples, squares can tile a plane. Four squares meet at a point; the sum of their interior angles is 4 x 90° = 360°.

EXAMPLE 5 A manufacturer of regular octagonal plates packages them in boxes with triangular padding in the corners. What are the measures of the interior angles of the triangular padding?

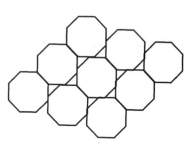

    A 30°, 60°, 90°
    B 40°, 50°, 90°
    C 45°, 45°, 90°
    D 60°, 60°, 60°

Strategy

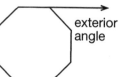

- First, you need to find the value of the *exterior* angle of a regular octagon.

- To find the measure of an exterior angle of a regular polygon, divide 360° by the number of its sides.

       360° ÷ 8 = 45°

- Since each exterior angle of a regular polygon is congruent, the triangle padding should have two 45° angles.

Solution   Choose C.

Try It 5

A manufacturer of regular brick polygons wants to combine two tiles and still have the new tiles tessellate. Which pair of regular polygons will tessellate or tile the plane?

    A hexagon and square
    B hexagon and pentagon
    C octagon and square
    D octagon and pentagon

120

Sample Virginia SOL Questions

1. What is the measure of angle *x* in the figure below?

    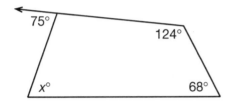

    A   105°

    B   90°

    C   63°

    D   53°

2. The line ℓ is a line of symmetry for figure *MNOPQRS*. What is the measure of ∠*OPQ*?

    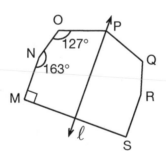

    F   70°

    G   140°

    H   160°

    J   320°

3. Diane is making a clock in the shape of a regular 9-gon from 9 pieces of wood. What is the measure of the angle between 2 of the pieces of wood?

    A   110°

    B   120°

    C   130°

    D   140°

4. Tyrone is making a sign in the shape of a regular octagon. What is the measure of each interior angle of the sign?

    F   125°

    G   135°

    H   145°

    J   155°

5. A manufacturer of regular brick polygons wants to create a new tile that uses 3 of the same type of polygon and that will also tesselate. What regular polygon will they use to create this new shape?

    A   all pentagons (5 sides)

    B   all hexagons (6 sides)

    C   all heptagons (7 sides)

    D   all octagons (8 sides)

121

CIRCLES

SOL G.10 *The student will investigate and use the properties of angles, arcs, chords, tangents, and secants to solve problems involving circles. Problems will include finding the area of a sector and applications of architecture, art, and construction.*

LINES AND CIRCLES

1 A line can intersect a circle at two points, or at one point, or not at all.

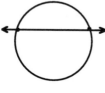
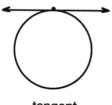

secant   tangent   no intersection

A line that intersects a circle at:
- two points is called a **secant**.
- one point is called a **tangent**.

2 A tangent to a circle is perpendicular to a radius drawn to the **point of tangency**.

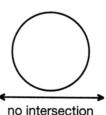

point of tangency

radius

- When two tangent segments are drawn to a circle from a point outside the circle, they are congruent:

$$\overline{PA} \cong \overline{PB}$$

- A line segment drawn from the point to the center of the circle forms congruent angles. $\angle 1 \cong \angle 2$

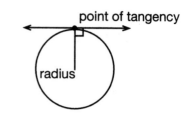

3 A **chord** is any line segment whose endpoints are on the circle. The diameter is the longest chord and passes through the center of the circle.

- In circle O, $\overline{CD}$ is a chord, $\overleftrightarrow{BC}$ is a secant, and $\overline{AB}$ is a tangent.

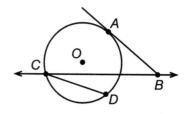
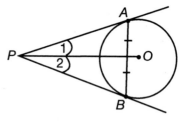

122

ARCS AND CIRCLES

4 An **arc** of a circle is any part of a circle and is named by its endpoints. The symbol ⌢ is placed over the letters to identify the arc. An arc is measured in degrees.

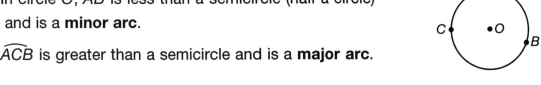

- In circle O, $\overarc{AB}$ is less than a semicircle (half a circle) and is a **minor arc**.

- $\overarc{ACB}$ is greater than a semicircle and is a **major arc**.

5 Parallel lines intercept equal arcs on a circle.

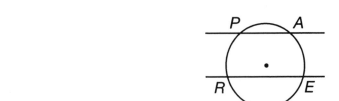

$\overline{PA} \parallel \overline{RE}$, then $m\overarc{AE} \cong m\overarc{PR}$

ANGLES AND CIRCLES

6 A **central angle** of a circle is an angle whose vertex is the center of the circle. The measure of the minor arc is the measure of the central angle. In the diagram, the measure of the central angle AOB is $x°$, so $m\overarc{AB} = x°$

7 An **inscribed angle** is an angle determined by two chords which intersect on the circle.

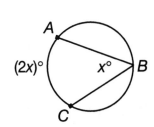

- The measure of an inscribed angle is half the degree measure of its intercepted arc.

- If the measure of arc $AC = (2x)°$, then the inscribed angle $ABC = \frac{1}{2} m\overarc{AC} = x°$

- An angle inscribed in a semicircle is a right angle.

- If a quadrilateral is inscribed in a circle, then the opposite angles are supplementary.

123

EXAMPLE 1 In the diagram on the right, $\overline{AB}$ is a diameter. What is the measure of $\overparen{DB}$ if $m\overparen{AD} = 50°$?

A   50°
B   120°
C   130°
D   160°

Strategy
- Since $\overline{AB}$ is a diameter, then the measure of $\overparen{ADB} = 180°$
$$\overparen{AD} + \overparen{DB} = \overparen{ADB}$$
- Substitute: $\qquad\qquad 50° + \overparen{DB} = 180°$
- Simplify: $\qquad\qquad m\overparen{DB} = 180° - 50° \rightarrow 130°$

Solution   Choose C.

Try It 1

Given the figure on the right with $m\overparen{AD} = 50°$, $m\overparen{CD} = 110°$, and $\overline{AB}$ is a diameter. What is the measure of $\overparen{DCB}$?

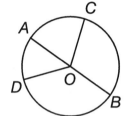

A   130°
B   160°
C   230°
D   260°

EXAMPLE 2 On the right, $\angle ABC$ is inscribed in circle O. What is the ratio of $m\angle ABC$ to $m\angle AOC$?

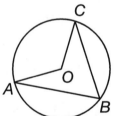

F   1 : 2
G   2 : 1
H   1 : 1
J   1 : 3

Strategy
- You need to use the definitions of a central angle and an inscribed angle to find the ratio of the angles.
  - $\angle ABC$ is an **inscribed** angle, and is $\frac{1}{2}$ the measure of $\overparen{AC}$.
  - $\angle AOC$ is a **central** angle, and is equal to the measure of $\overparen{AC}$.
- So if $m\overparen{AC}$ is 2, then $m\angle ABC : m\angle AOC$ would be 1 : 2.

Solution   Choose F.

Try It 2

Given the figure on the right, the m∠ABC = 60°.

What is the measure of ∠AOC?

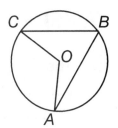

F   30°

G   60°

H   90°

J   120°

EXAMPLE 3 On the right, *PENTA* is a regular pentagon inscribed in a circle. What is the mP͡E?

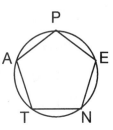

A   108°

B   72°

C   60°

D   50°

Strategy
- Since *PENTA* is an inscribed regular pentagon, all the sides are equal, and the measures of the arcs are also equal.

- To find the measure of any arc of an inscribed regular polygon, simply divide 360° by the number of sides in the polygon.
  360 ÷ 5 = 72

Solution   Choose B.

Try It 3

On the right is a regular polygon inscribed in a circle. What is the mF͡E?

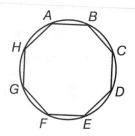

A 30°

B 45°

C 60°

D 72°

125

TANGENT, CHORD, AND SECANT ANGLES

8 The intersection of a tangent and a chord at the point of tangency forms an angle that is $\frac{1}{2}$ the degree measure of the intercepted arc.

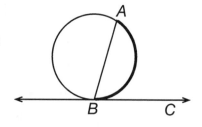

    Tangent $\overleftrightarrow{BC}$ and chord $\overline{AB}$ intersect at B.
    $m\angle ABC = \frac{1}{2}m\widehat{AB}$

9 The intersection of 2 chords inside a circle forms angles that are $\frac{1}{2}$ the **sum** of degree measure of the intercepted arcs.

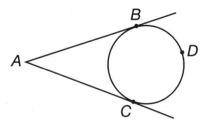

    Chords $\overline{FG}$ and $\overline{HJ}$ intersect at K.
    $m\angle JKG = \frac{1}{2}(m\widehat{FH} + m\widehat{JG})$

10 The intersection of 2 tangents forms an angle that is $\frac{1}{2}$ the degree measure of the **difference** between the major and minor arcs formed by the intersection with the circle.

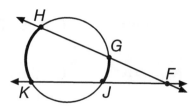

    Tangents $\overline{AB}$ and $\overline{AC}$, $m\angle A = \frac{1}{2}(m\widehat{BDC} - m\widehat{BC})$

11 The intersection of 2 secants outside the circle forms an angle that is $\frac{1}{2}$ the degree measure of the **difference** between the major and minor arcs formed by the intersection with the circle.

    Secants $\overline{FH}$ and $\overline{FK}$, $m\angle F = \frac{1}{2}(m\widehat{HK} - m\widehat{GJ})$

12 The intersection of a tangent and a secant outside the circle forms an angle that is $\frac{1}{2}$ the degree measure of the **difference** between the major and minor arcs formed by the intersection with the circle.

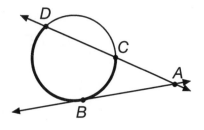

    Tangent $\overleftrightarrow{AB}$ and secant $\overleftrightarrow{AD}$, $m\angle A = \frac{1}{2}(m\widehat{BD} - m\widehat{BC})$

EXAMPLE 4 In the diagram on the right, chords $\overline{FG}$ and $\overline{HJ}$ intersect at K. m$\widehat{FH}$ = 40° and m∠JKG = 100°.

What is the m$\widehat{JG}$?

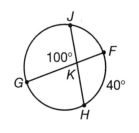

F   100°

G   140°

H   160°

J   200°

Strategy
- The intercepted arcs for ∠JKG are $\widehat{JG}$ and $\widehat{FH}$. You know that ∠JKG = $\frac{1}{2}$(m$\widehat{JG}$ + m$\widehat{FH}$).
- Substitute known values: 100° = $\frac{1}{2}$(40° + m$\widehat{FH}$)
- Simplify by multiplying by 2:   200 = 40° + m$\widehat{FH}$
- Simplify by subtracting 40°:   160° = $\widehat{FH}$

Solution   Choose H.

In the diagram at the right, chords $\overline{AB}$ and $\overline{CD}$ intersect at E. m$\widehat{AC}$ = 60°, and m∠ACE = 70°.

What is the m$\widehat{DB}$?

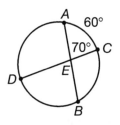

F   160°

G   140°

H   80°

J   70°

EXAMPLE 5 In the diagram on the right, tangents $\overline{PB}$ and $\overline{PC}$ are drawn to circle O, and m$\widehat{BC}$ = 100°. What is the measure of ∠P?

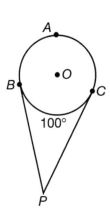

A   60°

B   80°

C   120°

D   180°

127

Strategy

- Since the degree measure of a circle is 360°, then $m\overset{\frown}{BAC} + m\overset{\frown}{BC} = 360°$
- Substitute known values: $\qquad m\overset{\frown}{BAC} + 100° = 360°$
- Simplify: $\qquad\qquad\qquad\qquad m\overset{\frown}{BAC} = 260°$
- You know that $\angle P = \frac{1}{2}(m\overset{\frown}{BAC} - m\overset{\frown}{BC})$,

  so substitute known values: $\qquad m\angle P = \frac{1}{2}(260° - 100°)$

  $\qquad\qquad\qquad\qquad\qquad\qquad m\angle P = \frac{1}{2}(160°) \to \angle P = 80°$

Solution   Choose B.

Try It 5

In the diagram on the right, tangents $\overline{PA}$ and $\overline{PA}$ are drawn to circle O and $m\overset{\frown}{AB} = 120°$. What is the measure of $\angle P$?

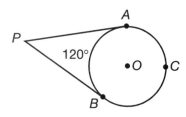

A 30°

B 60°

C 120°

D 180°

EXAMPLE 6 In the diagram on the right, $\angle ABC = 150°$, $\overset{\leftrightarrow}{CE}$ is a tangent and $\overline{BA}$ is a chord. What is $m\overset{\frown}{AB}$?

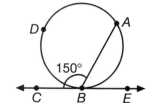

F 75°

G 60°

H 30°

J 15°

Strategy

- Since $\angle ABC$ and $\angle ABE$ form a linear pair, you know that $m\angle ABC$ plus $m\angle ABE = 180°$. Substitute known values and solve.
- $150° + \angle ABE = 180° \to \angle ABE = 30°$
- $\angle ABE = \frac{1}{2}m\overset{\frown}{AB} \to 30° = \frac{1}{2}m\overset{\frown}{AB} \to 2(30°) = 2(\frac{1}{2}m\overset{\frown}{AB}) \to 60° = \overset{\frown}{AB}$

Solution   Choose G.

128

Try It 6 In the diagram on the right, $\angle ABE = 20°$, $\overleftrightarrow{CE}$ is a tangent, and $\overline{BA}$ is a chord. What is $m\overparen{BDA}$?

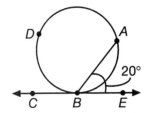

F   40°

G 160°

H 240°

J 320°

13 To find the **length of an arc**, first find its degree measure and set up the following ratio:

$$\frac{\text{degree measure of the arc}}{360}$$

then multiply it by the circumference. The answer is the **arc length**.

14 A **sector** of a circle is the region bound by two radii of the circle and their intercepted arc. The area of a sector of a circle is a fractional part of the area of the circle.

You can find the sector's area by $\dfrac{\text{degree measure of the arc}}{360}$ times the area of the circle.

EXAMPLE 7 Roma Pizzeria's small circular pizza is 12-inches in diameter. It is cut into 6 slices. To the nearest tenth of a square inch, what is the area of one slice?

A   9.4 sq. in.

B   18.8 sq. in.

C   37.6 sq. in.

D   113.0 sq. in.

Strategy

- The question is asking you to find the area of a sector, but first you need to find the area of the circle.

- The area is found by the formula: $A_\odot = \pi r^2$

  The radius, r, is $\frac{1}{2}$ the diameter, which is $\frac{1}{2} \cdot 12 = 6$.

  $A_\odot = 3.14 \cdot 6^2 \rightarrow A_\odot = 3.14 \cdot 36 \rightarrow A_\odot = 113.04$

129

- One slice is $\frac{1}{6}$ of the circle, so the area of the sector is $\frac{1}{6}$ of the area of the circle: $\frac{1}{6} \cdot 113.04 = 18.84$ or ≈ 18.8

Solution   Choose B.

Try It 7

Tom's Pizzeria's small circular pizza is 14 inches in diameter. It is cut into 8 slices. To the nearest tenth of a square inch, what is the area of one slice? Use $\pi = 3.14$.

A   153.9 sq. in.

B   38.6 sq. in.

C   19.2 sq. in.

D   8.7 sq. in.

EXAMPLE 8 How far does the tip of a 6-inch minute hand on a classroom clock travel in 20 minutes?

F   6.28 inches

G   12.56 inches

H   25.12 inches

J   37.68 inches

Strategy

- The question is asking you to find an arc length. but first you need to find the circumference of a circle. The tip of a minute hand on a clock defines a circle with a radius of 6-inches.

- The circumference is found by the formula: $C = 2r\pi$
  Substitute values: $C = 2 \cdot 6 \cdot 3.14$
  Simplify: $C = 12 \cdot 3.14 = 37.68$

- In 60 minutes, the movement of the tip of the minute hand completes a circle. In 20 minutes, the tip travels an arc length that is found by multiplying the ratio $\frac{20}{60}$ by the circumference.
  $\frac{20}{60} \cdot 37.68 = 12.56$ inches.

Solution   Choose G.

130

Try It 8

To the nearest hundredth, how far does the tip of a 1-inch minute hand on a wrist watch travel in 12 minutes?

F 6.28 inches

G 2.51 inches

H 1.26 inches

J 0.63 inches

TRY IT Answers: 1. C   2. J   3. B   4. H   5. B   6. J   7. C   8. H

Sample Virginia SOL Questions

1. Below, *PENTA* is a regular pentagon inscribed in a circle. What is the m∠*APE*?

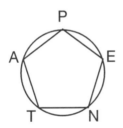

A   72°

B   108°

C   144°

D   216°

2. A dart board has a diameter of 50 cm and is divided into 20 congruent sectors. What is the area of one sector to the nearest hundredth?

F   7.85 cm²

G   39.25 cm²

H   78.50 cm²

J   98.13 cm²

3. Arc length of $\overset{\frown}{AB}$ = _____

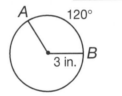

A   6.28 in.

B   9.42 in.

C   18.84 in.

D   28.26 in.

4. How far does the tip of a 9-inch minute hand on a classroom clock travel in 15 minutes?

F   2.25 in.

G   4.50 in.

H   7.065 in.

J   14.13 in.

5. Below, $\overleftrightarrow{PA} \parallel RE$. What is the is the measure of c?

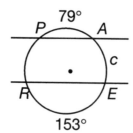

A 64°

B 116°

C 128°

D 232°

6. In the figure below, $\overleftrightarrow{AT}$ and $\overleftrightarrow{AN}$ are tangents. $m\angle ATN = 72°$. What is the measure of $\angle a$?

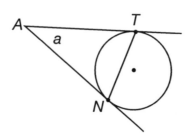

F 216°

G 144°

H 72°

J 36°

7. In the diagram below, what is the measure of $\overparen{UR}$?

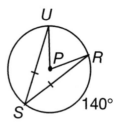

A 80°

B 140°

C 160°

D 240°

8. In the figure below, what is the measure of angle b?

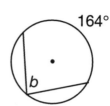

F 82°

G 164°

H 246°

J 328°

132

3-D MODELS

SOL G.12 *The student will make a model of a three-dimensional figure from a two-dimensional drawing and make a two-dimensional representation of a three-dimensional object. Models and representations will include scale drawings, perspective drawings, blueprints, or computer simulations.*

SOLIDS WITH POLYGONAL SURFACES

1 **Polyhedrons** are 3-D figures whose faces are all polygons. A **regular polyhedron** is one whose faces are all congruent, regular polygons.

- There are only five regular polyhedrons. These are: **tetrahedron** (4 sides), **cube** or **hexahedron** (6 sides), **octahedron** (8 sides), **dodecahedron** (12 sides), and **icosahedron** (20 sides).

2 Each polygon surface is called a **face**. Where two faces meet is called an **edge**. A **vertex** (*plural,* **vertices**) is a point where three or more faces meet.

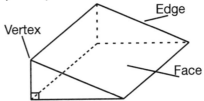

3 A **prism** is a solid that has two congruent polygonal bases that are parallel. These are connected by parallelogram faces (lateral faces). A **right prism** is one whose lateral edges are perpendicular to the bases (rectangular lateral faces).

- Prisms are named for the shape of their bases.

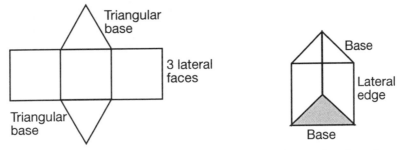

- The above prism is a **triangular prism**. A box-shaped prism is a a **rectangular prism** or **rectangular solid**.

133

4 A **pyramid** is a polyhedron with a polygon for its base and triangular faces that meet at a point (vertex). The shape of the base is used in naming the pyramid.

- A **regular pyramid** has a regular polygon base and lateral edges that are congruent.

- The **slant height** of a regular pyramid is the height of any of its lateral faces.

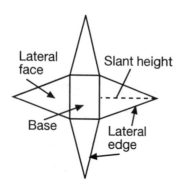

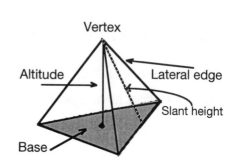

SOLIDS WITH CURVED SURFACES

5 A **cylinder** has 2 congruent circles as bases that are parallel, and its lateral surface is a parallelogram.

- The **axis** of a cylinder is the segment that joins the center of the bases. When the axis is perpendicular to the base, it is called a **right cylinder**. Otherwise it is oblique.

- The **altitude** (height) of a cylinder is a segment that is perpendicular to the bases. In a right cylinder, the axis is also an altitude

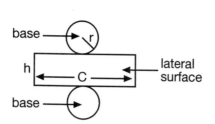

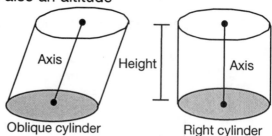

6 A **cone** has a circular base and a vertex.

- Its **axis** is the segment that joins the vertex and the center of the base.

- When the axis is perpendicular to the base, it is called a **right cone**, Otherwise it is **oblique**.

- The **slant height** is the distance from the vertex to the edge of the base.

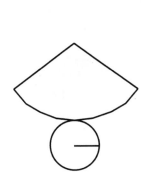

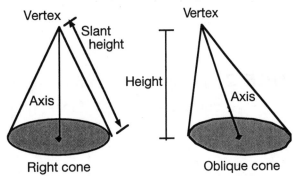

Right cone   Oblique cone

7 A **sphere** is the set of all points in space at a given distance from a given point.

- A **great circle** is the circle formed by cutting a sphere in half.

- The base of a **hemisphere** (half a sphere) is a great circle.

EXAMPLE 1 Using the 3 views of the 3-dimensional figure below, which of the following best describes the figure?

A pentagonal prism
B triangular prism
C square pyramid
D triangular pyramid

top   front   side

Strategy
- The top view shows that all the faces and base are triangles. This eliminates choices A and C.
- The top view also shows that the faces meet at a point. This means that the figure is a triangular pyramid (tetrahedron).

Solution   Choose D.

135

© *Educational Design. Photocopying or reproducing any part of this book is forbidden by law.*

Using the 3 views of a 3-dimensional figure on the right, which of the following best describes the figure?

A   Cone

B   Triangular prism

C   Triangular pyramid

D   Cylinder

Top   Front   Side

EXAMPLE 2 Look at the prism on the right. Which lists the correct number of faces, edges, and vertices, in that order, for the figure?

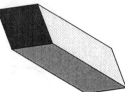

F   6, 12, 8

G   8, 12, 6

H   6, 8, 12

J   8, 12, 6

Strategy
- Since the base has four sides there are 4 lateral faces and 2 bases, so there are 6 faces. This fact eliminates choices G and J.
- For any prism with n-sided polygon for a base:

  $n + 2$ faces, $3n$ edges, and $2n$ vertices.
- There is an edge for each side of the base plus one for each lateral face: $4 + 4 + 4 = 12$
- There are 12 edges. This eliminates H.

Solution   Choose F.

Try It 2
Look at the prism on the right. Which lists the correct number of faces, edges, and vertices, in this order, for the figure?

F   7, 10, 15

G   7, 15, 10

H   10, 15, 7

J   10, 7, 15

8 A **net** is the 2-D diagram of a 3-D figure. If you
unfolded a 3-D figure and laid it flat on a table, you
would have a net. Imagine taking a rectangular prism
(a cereal box, for example) and unfolding it. The
figure would look something like the figure at the
right.

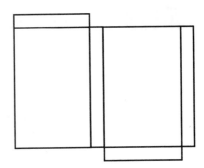

When you refold this net along the lines, you get
back the original cereal box (rectangular prism).

Nets are useful in constructing 3-D figures (cans, boxes, etc.) out of 2-D
materials (paper, metal, etc.).

EXAMPLE 3 Which net below can be used to make a hexagonal prism?

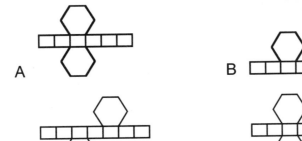

Strategy	• First, determine the number of faces of the prism. There are 2 parallel bases plus 6 rectangular sides that connect the edges of the bases.

• First, determine the number of faces of the prism. There are 2
parallel bases plus 6 rectangular sides that connect the edges of
the bases.

• A hexagon has 6 edges. There are 2 + 6 (8) faces on a hexagonal
prism. Choice D has only 7 faces, and so it can be eliminated.

• Eliminate Choice B, since the bases are on the same side of the
rectangle. They need to be on opposite sides.

• Eliminate Choice C, because there are too many (7) rectangluar
faces.

Solution   Choose A.

137

Which figure below is a net for a rectangular solid?

A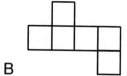

B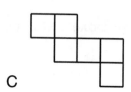

C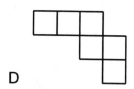

D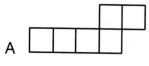

1. Which figure below is the base plan of the following shape?

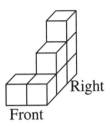

Right
Front

A

B

C

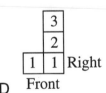

D

2. Which figure is a net for a triangluar prism?

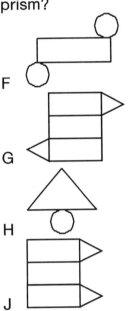

F

G

H

J

3. Look at the figure below. Which lists the correct number of faces, edges, and vertices, in this order, for the figure?

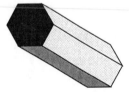

A 12 faces, 8 edges, 18 vertices
B 12 faces, 18 edges, 8 vertices
C 8 faces, 18 edges, 12 vertices
D 18 faces, 8 edges, 12 vertices

4. Using the 3 views below of a 3-dimensional figure, which of the following best describes the figure?

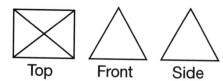

Top   Front   Side

F square pyramid
G rectangular pyramid
H rectangular prism
J triangular prism

5. Which one of the following nets will fold to make a pyramid with a square base?

A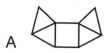

B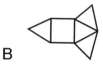

C

D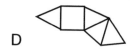

SURFACE AREA

SOL G.13 *The student will use formulas for surface area and volume of three-dimensional objects to solve practical problems. Calculators will be used to find decimal approximations for results.*

SURFACE AREA OF A POLYHEDRON

1 To find the **surface area** (S.A.) of a polyhedron, you first find the area of each face (including the bases), then add them together.

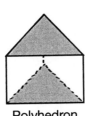

Polyhedron

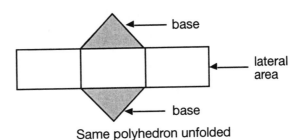

base

lateral area

base

Same polyhedron unfolded

EXAMPLE 1 A rectangular prism measures 4 m tall, 5 m wide, and 14 m long. What is its surface area?

A 23 m^2

B 146 m^2

C 292 m^2

D 280 m^2

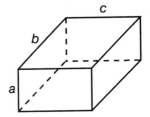

Strategy

- The prism has 6 faces that are made up of three different pairs of rectangles: *a* by *b*, *a* by *c*, and *b* by *c*. The surface area is equal to the sum of these faces. The formula is

$$2(a \cdot b) + 2(a \cdot c) + 2(b \cdot c)$$

- Substitute 4, 5, and 14 for *a*, *b*, and *c*:

$$2(4 \cdot 5) + 2(4 \cdot 14) + 2(5 \cdot 14)$$

- Multiply numbers in the parentheses: 2(20) + 2(56) + 2(70)

- Simplify by multiplication and add: 40 + 112 + 140 = 292

Solution   Choose C.

Try It 1

A rectangular prism has the following measurements: 12 cm tall, 4 cm wide, and 2 cm long. What is the surface area of this prism?

SURFACE AREA OF A PYRAMID

2 A **pyramid** is a polyhedron with one **base.** All other faces are triangles. The shape of the base is used in naming the pyramid. For example, the pyramid shown on the right would be called a **square pyramid**.

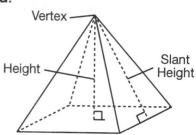

- The **height** of a pyramid is a perpendicular line from the base to the vertex.

- The **slant height** is a perpendicular line from the base edge to the vertex. This is also the height of the triangular face.

EXAMPLE 2 What is the surface area of this square pyramid?

F   60 sq ft
G   96 sq ft
H   156 sq ft
J   180 sq ft

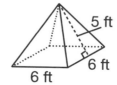

Strategy

- The surface area (**S.A.**) of a pyramid is the sum of the area of the base plus the area of the other triangular faces.
- The area of a square is s^2, or 6^2, which is 36 square feet.
- The area of a triangle is $\frac{1}{2}$ base • height. The base of each triangular face is 6 ft, and the height is 5, so the area of a triangular face is $= \frac{1}{2} • (5 • 6)$,or 15 square feet.

Solution

The total S.A. = 36 + 4(15) → 36 + 60 = 96 sq. ft. Choose G.

Try It 2

What is the surface area of this rectangular pyramid, shown with its faces spread out?

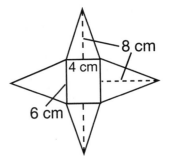

F   192 cm²

G   120 cm²

H   104 cm²

J   88 cm²

SURFACE AREA OF A CYLINDER

3 A **cylinder** has 2 congruent circles as bases, and its lateral surface is a rectangle.

- The surface area is the sum of the areas of the 2 circular bases and the area of the rectangle.

- The area of a base is πr^2, and the area of the rectangle is $\pi 2r \cdot h$.

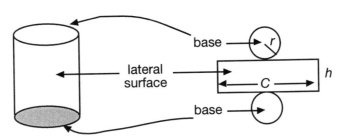

The surface area of a cylinder is $2(\pi r^2) + \pi 2r \cdot h$. For π we use either 3.14 or $\frac{22}{7}$.

EXAMPLE 3 Which amount of metal, to the nearest tenth of a cm, is used to make this tunafish can? Use $\pi = 3.14$.

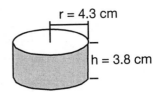

A   109.4 cm²

B   160.8 cm²

C   167.2 cm²

D   218.7 cm²

143

Strategy

- First, find the surface area of the cylinder. You begin by finding the area of a base. Use $A = \pi r^2$, $\pi = 3.14$ and $r = 4.3$.

$$A = 3.14 \cdot (4.3)^2 = 3.14 \cdot 4.3 \cdot 4.3 = 58.0586 \text{ cm}^2$$

- Now multiply this by 2 to find the area of the top and bottom bases:

$$2 \cdot 58.0586 = 116.1172 \text{ cm}^2$$

- Next, you need to find the area of the rectangular lateral side. Use $\pi 2rh$.

$$3.14 \cdot 2 \cdot 4.3 \cdot 3.8 = 102.6152 \text{ cm}^2$$

- To find the surface area add the area of the bases and the area of the lateral side.

$$116.1172 + 102.6152 = 218.7324 \text{ cm}^2$$

- Round 218.7324 to 218.7 cm².

Solution Choose D.

Try It 3

What is the surface area of the figure below?

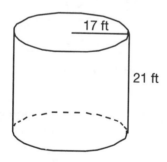

A 1814.92 sq. ft

B 2241.96 sq. ft

C 2935.90 sq. ft

D 4056.88 sq. ft

144

SURFACE AREA OF A CONE

4 A **cone** is a 3-D figure with one circular base and a curved surface that connects at a point. The diagrams will help you understand the formula for its surface area.

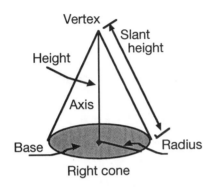

Right cone

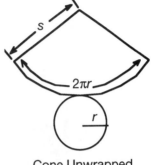

Cone Unwrapped

- SA = Base Area + Lateral Area.
- The area of the base is πr^2. The area of the lateral surface is πr times s, the slant height. The surface area of a cone equals $\pi r^2 + \pi r s$.

EXAMPLE 4 A pile of rock salt on the ground is in the shape of a cone with the dimensions shown below. It needs to be covered. To the nearest tenth, what is the minimum surface area of the tarp needed to cover this cone? Use $\pi = 3.14$.

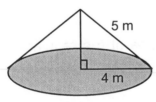

F   20 m^2

G   50.3 m^2

H   62.8 m^2

J   113.1 m^2

Strategy
- The question asks about the area of the UNcovered surface— that is, it does NOT include the area of the base, which is resting on the ground. You need to find the area of the lateral surface only.

- The formula for the lateral surface is πrs, where r is the radius, s is the slant height, and π is 3.14.

- $r = 4$ and $s = 5$, so the lateral surface is equal to $4 \cdot 5 \cdot 3.14$.

- $20 \cdot 3.14 = 62.8$.

Solution   Choose H.

Try It 4

What is the outside surface area of the ice cream cone?

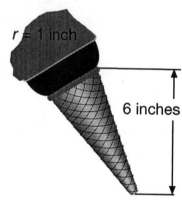

$r = 1$ inch

6 inches

F   3.14 sq in.

G   18.84 sq in.

H   19.84 sq in.

J   21.98 sq in.

EXAMPLE 5 What is the surface area of the regular pentagonal pyramid below?

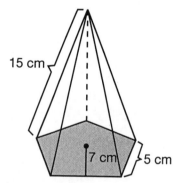

15 cm

7 cm   5 cm

A   3281.25 cm^2

B   392.5 cm^2

C   275 cm^2

D   205 cm^2

Strategy

- First find the area of the lateral faces by finding the area of one lateral face and multiplying it by the number of sides of the polygon.

    Use $\frac{1}{2}$ base • slant height for the area of one lateral face.

    $\frac{1}{2}$ • 5 cm • 15 cm • 5 sides = 187.5 cm^2

- Next find the area of the base polygon by multiplying the length of a side by the **apothem** (the perpendicular distance from the edge of the polygon to the center of the base), then by $\frac{1}{2}$, and finally by the number of sides of the polygon.

    5 cm • 7 cm • $\frac{1}{2}$ • 5 sides = 87.5 cm^2

- Finally, add these two areas to find the surface area of the pyramid:

    187.5 cm^2 + 87.5 cm^2 = 205 cm^2

Solution   Choose C.

Try It 5   What is the surface area of this regular hexagonal pyramid?

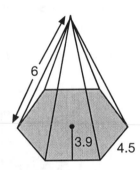

A   133.65

B   186.3

C   214.65

D   267.3

TRY IT Answers: 1. 160 cm^2 2. H   3. D   4. G   5. A

147

1. Which is the surface area of the following square pyramid?

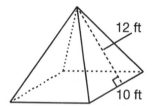

A 240 sq. ft
B 340 sq. ft
C 480 sq. ft
D 580 sq. ft

2. What is the surface area of the regular pentagonal pyramid below?

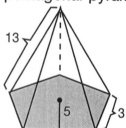

F 97.5
G 135
H 172.5
J 232

3. A rectangular prism has the following measurements: 0.8 m tall, 0.6 m wide, and 1.4 m long. What is the surface area of this prism?

A 0.672 m²
B 2.44 m²
C 4.88 m²
D 13.52 m²

4. A mulch pile is in the shape of a cone and needs to be covered. What is the lateral surface area of this cone? Use $\pi = \frac{22}{7}$

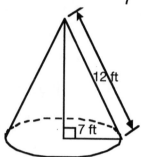

F 38 sq. ft
G 154 sq. ft
H 264 sq. ft
J 528 sq. ft

5. You are designing a new label for the following can of soup. What is the area of the label? Use $\pi = 3.14$

A 2901.4 cm²
B 1451.4 cm²
C 290.14 cm²
D 145.14 cm²

148

VOLUME

SOL G.13 *The student will use formulas for surface area and volume of three-dimensional objects to solve practical problems. Calculators will be used to find decimal approximations for results.*

1 **Volume** is the amount of space inside a 3-dimensional object. It is measured in the number of cubic units needed to fill the space. Each 3-dimensional figure has its own formula for finding its volume.

Here are all the volume formulas you will use in this lesson.

- Volume of a **prism:** $V = Bh$, where B = base area and h = height of prism

- Volume of a **pyramid:** $V = \frac{1}{3}Bh$, where B = base area and h = height of pyramid

- Volume of a **cylinder:** $V = \pi r^2 h$, where r = base radius and h = height of cylinder

- Volume of a **cone:** $V = \frac{1}{3}\pi r^2 h$, where r = base radius and h = height of cone

EXAMPLE 1 A fish tank is tilted on its edge as shown in the figure. What is the volume of the water in the tank?

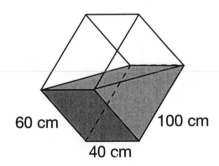

60 cm   100 cm   40 cm

    A 240,000 cm³

    B 120,000 cm³

    C   60,000 cm³

    D   30,000 cm³

Strategy • To find the volume of a prism, first find the area of the base and then multiply it by the height.

- The water forms a triangular prism. The base is a triangle, whose dimensions are 60 cm by 100 cm. $Area_\triangle = \frac{1}{2}b \cdot h$

  $\frac{1}{2} \cdot 60 \cdot 100 = 3,000$ cm^2

- The height of the triangular prism is 40 cm. Multiply it by the area of the base. $40 \cdot 3000$ cm^2 = 120,000 cm^3.

Solution   Choose B.

Try It 1   A fish tank is tilted on its edge as shown in the figure. The water reaches the midpoint of the longest side. What is the volume of the water in the tank?

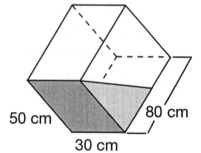

50 cm   30 cm   80 cm

A   120,000 cm^3

B   90,000 cm^3

C   60,000 cm^3

D   30,000 cm^3

EXAMPLE 2 A pyramid is placed inside a box. What is the volume of the empty space of the box?

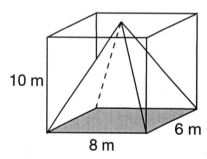

10 m   8 m   6 m

F   16 m^3

G   32 m^3

H   160 m^3

J   320 m^3

Strategy   • Since the volume of a pyramid is $\frac{1}{3}$ the volume of a rectangular prism with the same base and height, then the volume of the empty space is $\frac{2}{3}$ the volume of the prism.

150

- First find the area of the base and then multiply it by the height.

  Area$_\square$ = $b \cdot h$ The area of the base is $6 \cdot 8 = 48$ m^2.

- Next multiply the base area (48 m^2) by the height (10 m).

  48 m^2 $\cdot$ 10 m $= 480$ m^3

- Remember to multiply this product by $\frac{2}{3}$: $480 \cdot \frac{2}{3} = 320$ m^3.

Solution   Choose J.

Try It 2   Jordan places a hexagon-based pyramid candle in a box with the same base and height. What is the volume of the packing material needed to fill this box?

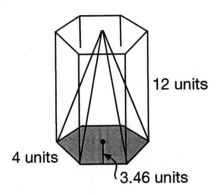

12 units

4 units

3.46 units

F   373.68 units^3

G   332.16 units^3

H   166.08 units^3

J   110.72 units^3

EXAMPLE 3 What is the volume of this cylinder? Use $\pi = 3.14$.

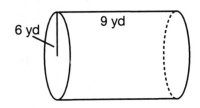

6 yd

9 yd

A   1,526.04 cubic yd

B   1,017.36 cubic yd

C   763.02 cubic yd

D   508.68 cubic yd

151

Strategy

- Just like finding the volume of a prism, you find the area of the base and then multiply it by the height. $Area_\bigcirc = \pi r^2$. The radius (r) is 6 yards.

    $A = 3.14 \cdot 6^2 \rightarrow 3.14 \cdot 36 \rightarrow 113.04$ square yards.

- Next, take this base area (113.04) and multiply if by the height (9).
    $113.04 \cdot 9 = 1,017.36$ cubic yards.

Solution

Choose B.

 Try It 3

A new soda can is being designed. It will be 25.5 cm tall and have a radius of 5 cm. Which is the largest number of cm^3 it will hold?

A   400 cm^3

B   900 cm^3

C   2,000 cm^3

D 10,000 cm^3

EXAMPLE 4 A cone is placed in a cylinder of the same circumference. The cone reaches $\frac{3}{4}$ of the depth of the cylinder.

What is the volume, to the nearest hundredth, of the empty space of the cylinder? Use $\pi = 3.14$.

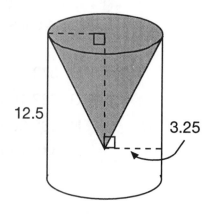

12.5

3.25

F 103.64

G 276.38

H 310.94

J 414.58

Strategy

- Finding the volume of a cone is similar to finding the volume of a pyramid. You find the area of the base, multiply it by the height, and then either multiply by $\frac{1}{3}$ or divide by 3. $Area_\bigcirc = \pi r^2$.

    $Area_\bigcirc = 3.14 \cdot 3.25 \cdot 3.25 \rightarrow 33.16625$

    Multiply by the height: $33.16625 \cdot (12.5 \cdot \frac{3}{4}) \approx 310.93359$,
    and then multiply by $\frac{1}{3}$ or divide by 3: $310.93359 \cdot \frac{1}{3} \approx 103.64453$

152

- To find the volume of a cylinder, you find the area of the base, and then multiply by the height.

  $\text{Area}_\bigcirc = \pi r^2$ (the area of the base of the cone),

  $33.16625 \cdot 12.5 \approx 414.57813$

- Now subtract the cone's volume from the cylinder's volume to get the volume of the empty space:

  $414.57813 - 103.64453 \approx 310.93359$

Solution

Choose H.

Try It 4 ▶ A cone is placed in a cylinder of the same circumference. The cone reaches $\frac{3}{5}$ of the depth of the cylinder. What is the volume of the empty space of the cylinder? Use $\pi = 3.14$.

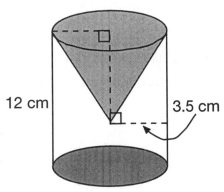

12 cm   3.5 cm

F   461.58 cm^3

G   369.26 cm^3

H   276.94 cm^3

J   92.32 cm^3

EXAMPLE 5 Which is the best height for a cylindrical water tank that has a 100,000 m^3 capacity and whose base has a radius of 25 m?

A   201 m

B   101 m

C   61 m

D   51 m

153

Strategy

- Since capacity refers to volume, you use the formula for finding the volume of a cylinder. $V = \pi r^2 h$. You are given the volume (100,000) and the radius. You need to solve for the height.

- Substitute the values into the formula. $100{,}000 = 3.14 \cdot 25^2 \cdot h$

- Simplify the equation by following the order of operations.
  $100{,}000 = 3.14 \cdot 25 \cdot 25 \cdot h \;\rightarrow\; 3.14 \cdot 625 \cdot h \rightarrow 1962.5h$
  $100{,}000 = 1962.5h.$

- Solve for h by dividing both sides of the equation by 1962.5.
  $$\frac{100000}{1962.5} = \frac{1962.5h}{1962.5} \rightarrow 50.955 \approx h.$$

- 50.955 rounded to the nearest 1 is 51.

Solution   Choose D.

Try It 5

Kate's aquarium is filled with 50.4 L of water. The length of the tank is 60 cm and the width is 35 cm. What is the depth of the water? (1 L = 1000 cm3.)

A 36 cm

B 32 cm

C 28 cm

D 24 cm

TRY IT Answers   *1. D*   *2. G*   *3. C*   *4. G*   *5. D*

1. Khufu's Pyramid, in Egypt, has a base of 230 m by 230 m and a height of 146.59 m. What is its volume?

   A 2,584,870 m³
   B 259,200 m³
   C 2,216,840 m³
   D 284,170 m³

2. What is the volume of this prism?

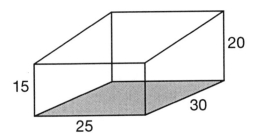

   F 9,000
   G 11,250
   H 13,125
   J 225,000

3. A cylinder has a volume of approximately 769 cm³. Its radius is 7 cm. What is the height of the cylinder to the nearest cm?

   A 4 cm
   B 5 cm
   C 6 cm
   D 7 cm

4. Zack's fish tank is 16 inches long, 10 inches wide and 12 inches tall. The volume of water in the tank is 800 cubic inches. How deep is the water?

   F 80 inches
   G 16 inches
   H   8 inches
   J   5 inches

5. A paper cup is filled to the rim with water. How much water does the cup hold?

   A 169.56 cm³
   B 113.04 cm³
   C 84.78 cm³
   D 56.52 cm³

6. Liz places a pyramid in a box with the same base and height. What is the volume of the packing material needed to fill this box?

   F   255 cm³
   G   765 cm³
   H 1530 cm³
   J 2295 cm³

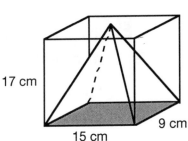

155

RATIO AND PROPORTION

SOL G.14 *The student, given similar geometric objects, will use proportional reasoning to solve practical problems; investigate relationships between linear, square, and cubic measures; and describe how changes in one of the measures of the object affect the others.*

1 **Ratios** are a way of comparing two numbers, quantities, or variables. You can write a ratio any of three ways: 5 to 7   5 : 7 $\frac{5}{7}$

2 A **proportion** is a statement that two ratios are equal. Four values (numbers, quantities, or variables) are used in a proportion. If any three are known, then the fourth can be determined.

Proportions can be written in two ways:
$$1 : 5 :: 4 : 20 \quad \text{or} \quad \frac{1}{5} = \frac{4}{20}$$

Both are read as "1 is to 5 as 4 is to 20."

- If *a*, *b*, *c*, and *d* are non-zero numbers and $\frac{a}{b} = \frac{c}{d}$, then the following properties are helpful in solving proportions.

Cross Product $ad = bc$

Exchange Means $\frac{a}{b} = \frac{c}{d} \rightarrow \frac{a}{c} = \frac{b}{d}$

Reciprocal $\frac{a}{b} = \frac{c}{d} \rightarrow \frac{b}{a} = \frac{c}{d}$

Adding denominators to numerators: $\frac{a}{b} = \frac{c}{d} \rightarrow \frac{a+b}{b} = \frac{c+d}{d}$

3 In a scale drawing, the **scale** is a ratio that compares the drawing distances or measures to the real-world distances or measures.

The **scale factor** of similar figures is the size of the change from the original figure. It is also the ratio of the corresponding sides.

EXAMPLE 1 A map of Virginia has a scale of 3 cm : 9 km. Two cities are 14.7 cm apart on the map. What is the actual distance between the two cities?

    A   44.1 km

    B   46.7 km

    C   47 km

    D 441 km

Strategy

- First set up the proportion of two ratios.

$$\frac{\text{map}}{\text{actual}} = \frac{\text{map distance}}{\text{actual distance}} \rightarrow \frac{3}{9} = \frac{14.7}{a}$$

- Cross multiply: $3a = 9 \cdot 14.7 \rightarrow 3a = 132.3$

- Since a is multiplied by 3, use the inverse operation, division, to solve the equation:

$$a = \frac{132.3}{3} \rightarrow a = 44.1$$

Solution   Choose A.

Try It 1

A map of Virginia is drawn with a scale of 3 inch = 50 miles. Two cities are $2\frac{1}{4}$ inches apart on the map. What is the actual distance between the two cities?

    A 17.5 miles

    B 37.5 miles

    C 56.25 miles

    D 112.5 miles

EXAMPLE 2 $\triangle ABD$ is similar to $\triangle ECD$. Which is the value of h?

    F 1.25

    G 1.5

    H 2.67

    J 6

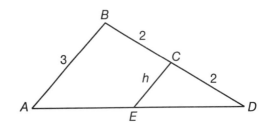

157

Strategy

- First set up the ratio of the sides of △ABD equal to the corresponding sides of △ECD.

$$\frac{AB}{EC} = \frac{BD}{CD}$$

- Substitute the values for the sides: $\frac{3}{h} = \frac{4}{2}$

- Cross multiply: $3 \cdot 2 = 4 \cdot h$

- Divide both sides by 4 and simplify.

$$\frac{3 \cdot 2}{4} = \frac{4 \cdot h}{4} \rightarrow \frac{6}{4} = h \rightarrow \frac{3}{2} = h \rightarrow 1.5 = h$$

Solution   Choose G.

Try It 2

Rectangles *ABCD* and *AGFE* are similar. The m$\overline{AB}$ = 5.2, the m$\overline{BC}$ = 7.8, and the m$\overline{AG}$ = 2.6. Which is the measure of $\overline{AE}$?

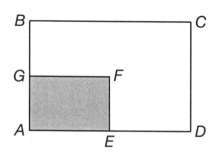

F   1.3
G   2.6
H   3.9
J   5.2

4 When figures are similar:

- The ratio of the *areas* is equal to the ratio of any two corresponding lengths squared.

$$\frac{\text{area of square}_1}{\text{area of square}_2} = \left(\frac{3}{6}\right)^2 = \left(\frac{1}{2}\right)^2 = \frac{1}{4}$$

- The ratio of the *volumes* is equal to the ratio of any two corresponding lengths cubed.

$$\frac{\text{volume of cube}_1}{\text{volume of cube}_2} = \left(\frac{3}{6}\right)^3 = \left(\frac{1}{2}\right)^3 = \frac{1}{8}$$

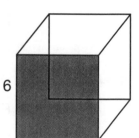

EXAMPLE 3 Rectangular prisms *A* and *B*, are similar. The edge of Prism *B* is 3 times that of prism *A*. How many times the volume of prism *A* is prism *B*?

    A 3

    B 9

    C 12

    D 27

Strategy
- Let the edge of prism $A = s$, so the volume $= s^3$.
- Then the edge of prism B is $3s$, and the volume $= (3s)^3$ or $27s^3$.
- The volume of prism $B = 27s^3$ which is 27 times the volume of prism A, s^3.

Solution   Choose D.

Try It 3

Billy, a metal sculptor, has just made a small, solid bronze statue and it weighs 39 pounds. He plans to make a full-scale version of the statue, which will be 4 times as large in each dimension. How much will the larger bronze statue weigh?

    A 4992 pounds

    B 2496 pounds

    C   624 pounds

    D   156 pounds

EXAMPLE 4 The ratio of the corresponding edges of two similar triangular prisms, *A* and *B*, is 3 to 2. What is the ratio of the surface area of prism *A* to the surface area of prism *B*?

    F $\dfrac{9}{8}$

    G $\dfrac{3}{2}$

    H $\dfrac{9}{4}$

    J. $\dfrac{4}{9}$

Strategy
- You know that the figures are similar, and the ratio of one area to another is equal to the ratio of any two corresponding lengths squared.

- In this case, $\dfrac{\text{edge of triangular prism } A}{\text{edge of triangular prism } B} = \dfrac{3}{2}$

- Square the ratio of the edges $\dfrac{3^2}{2^2}$ to get the ratio of the areas: $\dfrac{9}{4}$

Solution   Choose H.

Try It 4

Cube C has an edge of 2. Each edge is increased by 50%, creating a second cube D. What is the ratio of the volume of cube C to cube D?

F $\dfrac{4}{9}$

G $\dfrac{9}{4}$

H $\dfrac{27}{8}$

J $\dfrac{8}{27}$

EXAMPLE 5 Use the figure on the right. $\triangle ABC$ is a right triangle. What is the length of $\overline{AD}$?

A 180

B 200

C 220

D 240

300 m
500 m
400 m
A, C, D, B

Strategy
- The altitude divides the original triangle into two smaller triangles that are similar to each other and to the original triangle.

$$\dfrac{AD}{CD} = \dfrac{CD}{DB}, \quad \dfrac{AB}{AC} = \dfrac{AC}{AD}, \quad \text{and} \quad \dfrac{AB}{CB} = \dfrac{CB}{DB}$$

- $\dfrac{AD}{AC} = \dfrac{AC}{AB} \rightarrow \dfrac{AD}{300} = \dfrac{300}{500} \rightarrow 500(\overline{AD}) = 90{,}000.$

- $m\overline{AD} = 180$

Solution   Choose A.

160

Try It 5

Use the figure on the right. $\triangle XYZ$ is a right triangle. What is the length of $\overline{XZ}$?

A $20\sqrt{5}$

B   16

C $8\sqrt{5}$

D $6\sqrt{5}$

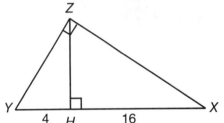

EXAMPLE 6 $\overline{DF}$ is an enlargement of $\overline{AC}$. $\overline{DF}$ is 4.5 units long and $\overline{AC}$ is 1.2 units long. How many units long is $\overline{DE}$?

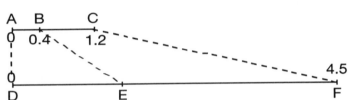

F   1.5

G   2.25

H   0.8.

J   2.3

Strategy

• First set up the proportion of the ratio of the line segments of $\overline{ABC}$ equal to the corresponding line segments of $\overline{DEF}$.

$$\frac{AB}{AC} = \frac{DE}{DF} \quad \rightarrow \quad \frac{0.4}{1.2} = \frac{s}{4.5}$$

• Cross multiply. $1.2s = 0.4 \cdot 4.5 \quad \rightarrow \quad 1.2s = 1.8$

• s is multiplied by 1.2: use division to solve the equation.

$$1.2s = 1.8 \quad \rightarrow \quad s = \frac{1.8}{1.2} \quad \rightarrow \quad s = 1.5$$

Solution   Choose F.

Try It 6

Paul enlarges a 7.62-cm wide and 12.7 cm-high photo to a 60.96-cm wide poster. Which is the height of the enlargement?

F   20.32 cm

G   36.576 cm

H   48.26 cm

J   101.6 cm

161

Sample Virginia SOL Questions

1. $\triangle ABC \sim \triangle ADE \sim \triangle AFG$. What is the ratio of the area of $\triangle ADE \sim \triangle AFG$?

   A   3:1
   B   3:2
   C   4:9
   D   9:4

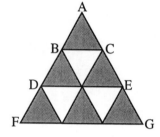

2. Given the figure below, what is the length of $\overline{US}$?

   F   2
   G   4
   H   8
   J   12

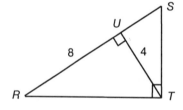

3. On the blueprints for a new home, a room measures $1\frac{5}{8}$ in. by $1\frac{1}{4}$ in. The scale on the blueprint is 1 in. : 12 ft. What are the dimensions of the actual room?

   A   12 ft x 18.5 ft
   B   15 ft x 18.5 ft
   C   15 ft x 19.5 ft
   D   12 ft x 19.5 ft

4. A map of Virginia is drawn with a scale of 4 inch = 60 miles. Two cities are $5\frac{3}{4}$ inches apart on the map. What is the actual distance between the two cities?

   F   345 miles
   G   143.75 miles
   H   86.25 miles
   J   15 miles

5. Rectangles $ABCD$ and $AGFE$ are similar. The m$\overline{AB}$ = 7.6, the m$\overline{AE}$ = 5.7, and the m$\overline{AG}$ = 3.8. Which is the measure of $\overline{BC}$?

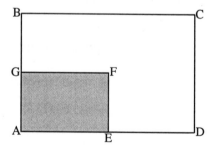

   A   1.9
   B   2.85
   C   9.5
   D   11.4

DISTANCE AND MIDPOINT

SOL G.2 *The student will use pictorial representations, including computer software and coordinate methods, to solve problems involving symmetry and transformation. This will include using formulas for finding **distance, midpoint**, [and slope].*

THE COORDINATE PLANE

1 A **coordinate plane** is a grid that has both a **horizontal** (*x*) **axis** and **vertical** (*y*) **axis** that divide it into 4 **quadrants**. The **origin** is where the axis cross. It has a value of (0,0).

2 A pair of numbers in parentheses, called an **ordered pair**, is used to locate an exact position on a coordinate plane.

- The first number of an ordered pair is found on the **x-axis** (horizontal).

- The second number is found on the **y-axis** (vertical).

Coordinate Plane

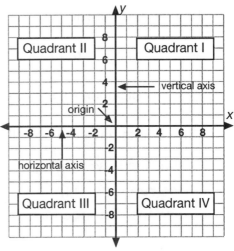

3 All the points in a quadrant have similar positive and negative values:

- Quadrant I points have both positive *x* and positive *y* values.
- Quadrant II points have negative *x* and positive *y* values.
- Quadrant III points have both negative *x* and negative *y* values.
- Quadrant IV points have positive *x* and negative *y* values.

DISTANCE

4 You can find the distance between any two points on the coordinate plane by using the **distance formula**—a generalization of the Pythagorean theorem.

On the simplified diagram of the coordinate plane at the right, the distance between points A and B is the hypotenuse of a right triangle whose legs are the rise and the run.

So, according to the Pythagorean theorem—

$$\text{distance (d)} = \sqrt{\text{rise}^2 + \text{run}^2}$$

If the points have the coordinates (x_1, y_1) and (x_2, y_2), then—

the **rise** is $(y_2 - y_1)$ and
the **run** is $(x_2 - x_1)$
and the **distance** (d) $= \sqrt{\text{rise}^2 + \text{run}^2} \rightarrow \sqrt{(y_2 - y_1)^2 + (x_2 - x_1)^2}$

MIDPOINT

5 The **midpoint** of a segment is the average of the coordinates of the endpoints. If the coordinates of a segment's endpoints are (x_1, y_1) and (x_2, y_2), then the midpoint is the point $\left(\dfrac{x_1 + x_2}{2}, \dfrac{y_1 + y_2}{2}\right)$.

EXAMPLE 1 What is the distance between points (–2,4) and (4,–4)?

> A   6
> B   8
> C   10
> D   36

164

Strategy
- First, it does not matter which point is (x_1, y_1), so we will use the first one $(-2, 4)$.

- Next, assign the second point to $(x_2, y_2) \rightarrow (4, -4)$.

- Use the distance formula: $d = \sqrt{(x_2 - x_1)^2 + (y_2 - y_1)^2}$

  Substitute values: $d = \sqrt{(4 - (-2))^2 + (-4 - 4)^2}$

  Simplify: $d = \sqrt{6^2 + (-8)^2}$

  $d = \sqrt{36 + 64} \rightarrow d = \sqrt{100} = 10$

Solution   Choose C.

 What is the distance between point A and B in the figure on the right?

A $\sqrt{5}$

B $\sqrt{13}$

C $\sqrt{39}$

D $\sqrt{97}$

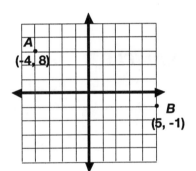

EXAMPLE 2 The coordinates of diameter $\overline{AB}$ of circle H are $A(2,4)$ and $B(-16, y)$. The coordinate of the center is $(-7, 6)$. What is the value of y?

F   7

G   8

H   14

J   16

Strategy
- The center of the circle is the midpoint of the diameter. Since you only need to find y, use:

  $y = \dfrac{y_1 + y_2}{2}$ and substitute values: $6 = \dfrac{4 + y}{2}$

165

- Simplify by multiplying by 2: $\quad 2 \cdot 6 = 2 \cdot \dfrac{4+y}{2} \ \rightarrow \ 12 = 4 + y$

- Simplify by adding 4: $\quad 12 + {-4} = -4 + 4 + y \ \rightarrow \ 8 = y$

Solution   Choose G.

Try It 2

On a coordinate plane, the midpoint of $\overline{AB}$ is the point $M(6,-2)$. One endpoint of $\overline{AB}$ is the point $B(-1,8)$. What are the coordinates of the other endpoint?

    F   (12,–13)

    G (–13,12)

    H (13,–12)

    J   (–12,13)

EXAMPLE 3 In the figure, point M is the midpoint of CD. The length of $\overline{CM}$ is $5x - 9$ and the length of $\overline{MD}$ is $2x + 6$. What is the length of $\overline{CD}$?

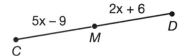

    A   5

    B   15

    C   16

    D   32

Strategy

- Since M is the midpoint of $\overline{CD}$, then $m\overline{CM} = m\overline{MD}$. Therefore: $5x - 9 = 2x + 6$ and you need to solve for x.

- $5x - 9 + 9 = 2x + 6 + 9$ Add 9 to both sides. $\ \rightarrow \ 5x = 2x + 15$

  $5x - 2x = 2x - 2x + 15$ Subtract $2x$ from both sides. $\ \rightarrow \ 3x = 15$

  $\dfrac{3x}{3} = \dfrac{15}{3}$ Divide both sides by 3 $\ \rightarrow \ x = 5$

- $m\overline{CD} = m\overline{CM} + m\overline{MD}$ or $(5x - 9) + (2x + 6)$. Substitute 5 for x.

- $[5(5) - 9] + [2(5) + 6] \quad \rightarrow \quad [25 - 9] + [10 + 6] \quad \rightarrow \quad [16] + [16] = 32$

Solution   Choose D.

Try It 3

The midpoint of $\overline{AB}$ is C. The length of $\overline{AC}$ is $2x + 7$ and of $\overline{CB}$ is $6x - 13$. What is the value of x?

A   5

B   10

C   17

D   34

EXAMPLE 4 The coordinates of point A in the figure below are $(-4,-0.5)$, and the coordinates of point B are $(-0.5,3)$. The line of symmetry for the figure passes through point $(1.5,-2.5)$ on $\overline{EF}$. Through what point on $\overline{AB}$ does it pass?

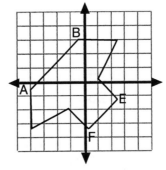

F $(-1.75,1.25)$

G $(-2.25,1.25)$

H $(-2.25,1.75)$

J $(-1.25,-1.50)$

Strategy

- The line of symmetry passes through the midpoint of $\overline{AB}$, so you need to find the coordinates of the midpoint: $\left(\dfrac{x_1 + x_2}{2}, \dfrac{y_1 + y_2}{2}\right)$.

- Substitute $(-4,-0.5)$ for (x_1, y_1) and $(-0.5,3)$ for (x_2, y_2) and simplify.

$$\frac{x_1 + x_2}{2} \rightarrow \frac{-4 + -0.5}{2} \rightarrow \frac{-4.5}{2} \rightarrow -2.25$$

$$\frac{y_1 + y_2}{2} \rightarrow \frac{-0.5 + 3}{2} \rightarrow \frac{2.5}{2} \rightarrow 1.25$$

- The coordinates of the midpoint are $(-2.25,1.25)$.

Solution

Choose G.

167

Try It 4

$\triangle ABC$ is reflected over a line. Point $A(-4, 4.5)$ and its image point $A'(6.5, -1.5)$ are equidistant from the line of reflection. What is one coordinate of the line of reflection?

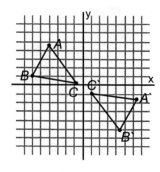

F   (1.25, 3)

G   (1.25, 1.5)

H   (5.25, 1.5)

J   (5.25, 3)

EXAMPLE 5   In the figure on the right, what is the area of $\triangle BAT$ in square units?

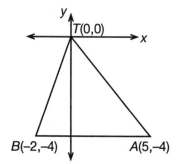

A   6

B   12

C   14

D   28

Strategy

- $\text{Area}_\triangle = \dfrac{\text{base} \times \text{height}}{2}$. A convenient base is $\overline{BA}$. A convenient height is the vertical distance from T to $\overline{BA}$. The length of $\overline{BA}$ is 7.

- The vertical distance from T to $\overline{BA}$ is 4.

- $\text{Area}_\triangle = \dfrac{\text{base} \times \text{height}}{2} = \dfrac{7 \times 4}{2} = \dfrac{28}{2} = 14$

Solution   Choose C.

Try It 5

In the figure, what is the area of $\triangle MAP$ in square units?

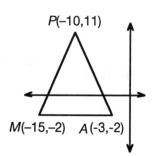

A $72\frac{1}{2}$

B   78

C $83\frac{3}{4}$

D   87

168

EXAMPLE 6 In the figure on the right, what is the perimeter of △*FUN*?

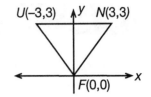

F 18

G $12 + 3\sqrt{2}$

H $6 + 6\sqrt{2}$

J $6 + 3\sqrt{2}$

Strategy
- First, use the distance formula, counting, or your knowledge of right triangles to find the lengths of the 3 sides. Then add them to find the perimeter of △*FUN*.

$$m\overline{UN} = 6 \quad \text{by counting } -3 \text{ to } 3$$

$\overline{FU}$ and $\overline{FN}$ are each the hypotenuse of a 3, 3, $3\sqrt{2}$ isosceles right triangle. Therefore $\overline{FU} = 3\sqrt{2}$ and $\overline{FN} = 3\sqrt{2}$.

- The perimeter of △*FUN* $= 6 + 3\sqrt{2} + 3\sqrt{2} \;\rightarrow\; 6 + 6\sqrt{2}$.

Solution Choose H.

Try It 6

In the figure below, what is the perimeter of △*FAR*?

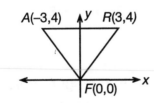

F 8

G 11

H 13

J 16

Sample Virginia SOL Questions

1. In the figure below, point M is the midpoint of $\overline{CD}$. What is the length of $\overline{CD}$?

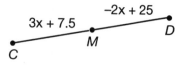

A 10.5

B 18

C 21.5

D 36

2. What is the length of a line segment whose endpoints have coordinates (-1,1) and (2,3)?

F $\sqrt{5}$

G $\sqrt{13}$

H 5

J 13

3. A segment has endpoints of (6,1) and (4, y) with a midpoint of (5,3). What is the value of y?

A 2

B 3

C 5

D 6

4. In the figure below, what is the perimeter of $\triangle CAR$?

F $10 + 2\sqrt{13}$

G $14 + 2\sqrt{13}$

H $18 + 2\sqrt{13}$

J $22 + 2\sqrt{13}$

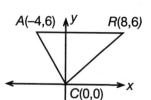

5. The coordinates of point D is (-1.5,-3.5) and point E is (-4.5,-0.5). The line of symmetry for the figure below passes through point (1,2) on $\overline{AB}$ and through what point on $\overline{DE}$?

A (-3,-2)

B (-1.5,-1.5)

C (-2.5,-2)

D (-3,-1.5)

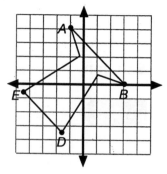

6. In the figure below, what is the area of $\triangle DAP$?

F $6\frac{2}{3}$

G $9\frac{3}{4}$

H $11\frac{1}{4}$

J $12\frac{1}{2}$

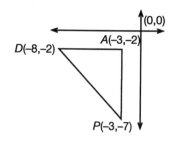

170

SLOPE

SOL G.2 *The student will use pictorial representations, including computer software and coordinate methods to solve problems involving symmetry and transformation. This will include using formulas for finding [distance, midpoint], and* **slope.**

1 **Slope** is a rate of change. The slope of a line is defined as $\frac{\text{rise}}{\text{run}}$, that is:

$$\frac{\text{vertical change}}{\text{horizontal change}} = \frac{\text{change in } y}{\text{change in } x} = \frac{\text{difference in } y\text{-coordinates}}{\text{difference in } x\text{-coordinates}} = \frac{y_2 - y_1}{x_2 - x_1}.$$

2 Lines drawn in a coordinate plane are *always read left to right*. This helps in describing the slope of a line in the coordinate plane.

There are 4 possible slopes, or orientations:

- An *increasing* function or **uphill line** has a **positive** slope.

- A *decreasing* function or **downhill line** has a **negative** slope.

- A *horizontal* line represents a **constant** function that has a **zero** slope.

- A *vertical* line is NOT A FUNCTION, so it has an "undefined" or **no** slope.

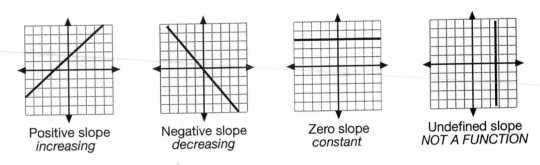

Positive slope
increasing

Negative slope
decreasing

Zero slope
constant

Undefined slope
NOT A FUNCTION

3 **Parallel lines** always have the *same* slope. All horizontal lines are parallel to the *x*-axis. All vertical lines are parallel to the *y*-axis.

4 **Perpendicular lines** always have *opposite sign reciprocal* slopes, and the product of their slopes is equal to –1 For example:

- If a line has a slope of 2, a perpendicular to it has a slope of $-\frac{1}{2}$.

- The product of their slopes is $2 \cdot -\frac{1}{2} = -1$

171

5 An equation of a line is written in either of two common forms:

   a The **general form** is $Ax + By = C$, where A, B, and C are constants (numbers)

   b The **slope-intercept** form is $y = mx + b$, where m is the slope and b is the y-intercept.

EXAMPLE 1 What is the slope of the line passing through the points $A(3, -1)$ and $B(8, -5)$?

     A $\dfrac{-4}{5}$

     B $\dfrac{-6}{11}$

     C $\dfrac{-5}{4}$

     D $\dfrac{9}{4}$

Strategy

- Let $(3, -1)$ be (x_1, y_1) and $(8, -5)$ be (x_2, y_2).
- Slope $(m) = \dfrac{y_2 - y_1}{x_2 - x_1}$
- Substitute values: $\dfrac{-5 - (-1)}{8 - 3}$ and simplify: $\dfrac{-4}{5}$.
- $m = \dfrac{-4}{5}$

Solution

Choose A.

Try It 1

What is the slope of the line passing through the points $A(7,6)$ and $B(2,4)$?

     A $\dfrac{7}{2}$

     B $\dfrac{5}{2}$

     C $\dfrac{10}{9}$

     D $\dfrac{2}{5}$

EXAMPLE 2 $\overline{AB}$, $\overline{BC}$, $\overline{CD}$, and $\overline{DA}$ form a tilted rectangle in a coordinate plane. The slope of the line AB is $\frac{-4}{5}$. What is the slope of line BC?

F $\frac{-5}{4}$

G $\frac{-4}{5}$

H $\frac{1}{5}$

J $\frac{5}{4}$

Strategy
- Since ABCD is a rectangle, adjacent sides ($\overline{AB}$ and $\overline{BC}$) are perpendicular. and their slopes are reciprocals with opposite signs.
- Since the slope of line AB is negative, a line perpendicular must have an opposite, or positive, slope. This eliminates choices F and G.
- To find the reciprocal of $\frac{4}{5}$, divide 1 by $\frac{4}{5}$ = $\frac{5}{4}$.

Solution
Choose J.

Try It 2

Complete this statement: "Two lines are perpendicular to each other if and only if the product of their slopes is _____ ."

F $\frac{-1}{2}$

G –1

H 1

J $\frac{1}{2}$

EXAMPLE 3 In Parallelogram *ABCD*, the coordinates of three of the vertices are $A(-1, -2)$, $B(5, -2)$, and $C(7, 3)$. What are the coordinates of vertex D?

A (–1, 3)

B (1, 3)

C (5, 3)

D (13, 3)

173

Strategy

- The opposite sides of a parallelogram are parallel and equal in length, so $m\overline{AB} = m\overline{DC}$.

- Points A and B both have the same y-value, which means that AB is horizontal and its length is the difference of the x-coordinates.

- $m\overline{AB}$ is $5 - (-1) = 6$. Therefore, the length of the side opposite $\overline{AB}$, $\overline{DC}$ is also 6.

- The x-coordinate of point D is $7 - x = 6 \rightarrow x = 1$. The y-coordinate of D is the same as the y-coordinate of C. So the coordinates of D are (1, 3).

Solution   Choose B.

Try It 3

In Parallelogram $ABCD$, the coordinates of three of the vertices are $A(0, 4)$, $B(6, 4)$, and $C(3, -1)$. What are the coordinates of vertex D?

A   (3, –1)

B   (–3, –1)

C   (–6, –1)

D   (6, –1)

6 If you know a point on a line and the slope of the line, then you can find the general form of an equation of a line, using the following formula:

$$y - y_1 = m(x - x_1) \text{ where } m \text{ is the slope}$$

EXAMPLE 4 What is the equation of the line which passes through points (2,7) and (8, –1)?

F $4x + 3y = 29$

G $4x + 3y = 19$

H $4x + 3y = 15$

J $4x + 3y = 13$

Strategy

- First, find the slope of the line by using the formula: $\dfrac{y_2 - y_1}{x_2 - x_1}$

174

- Let (8, –1) be (x_1, y_1), and let (2, 7) be (x_2, y_2).
- Substitute values: $\dfrac{7-(-1)}{2-8}$ and simplify: $\dfrac{-4}{3}$.
- Remember, the equation of the line passing through the point (x_1, y_1) and whose slope is m is: $y - y_1 = m(x - x_1)$.
- Substitute values: $y - -1 = \dfrac{-4}{3}(x - 8)$
- Simplify:
$$3(y - -1) = -4(x - 8)$$
$$3y - -3 = -4x + 32$$
$$3y + +3 = -4x + 32$$
$$3y + 4x = 29$$

Solution   Choose F.

Try It 4

What is the equation of the line which passes through points (3,4) and (9, –2)?

F $y - x = 7$
G $y + x = 7$
H $3y - 4x = 11$
J $4y - 3x = 11$

EXAMPLE 5 What is the *slope-intercept form* equation of the line which has a slope of 7 and passes through point (–3,–26)?

A $y = 7x$
B $y = 7x - 5$
C $y = 7x + 5$
D $y = 7x - 12$

Strategy
- First, the slope-intercept form of the equation of the line is $y = mx + b$.
- You know the slope, m, is 7 and you substitute the coordinates of the point for x and y. $\qquad -26 = 7(-3) + b$
- Solve this equation for b. $\qquad -26 = -21 + b$
- Simplify by adding 21 to both sides. $\quad -26 + 21 = -21 + 21 + b.$
$$-5 = b$$

175

- Rewrite the slope-intercept equation, substituting in the values for m and b:
  $$y = 7x + -5$$

Solution   Choose A.

> **Try It 5**

What is the *slope-intercept form* equation of the line which has a slope of 5 and passes through point (–6,–26)?

A $y = 5x + 4$

B $y = 5x - 4$

C $y = 5x + 32$

D $y = 5x - 32$

TRY IT Answers: 1. D   2. G   3. B   4. G   5. A

Sample Virginia SOL Questions

1. In the coordinate plane, line $\ell \perp p$. The slope of line ℓ is $\frac{2}{m}$. What is the slope of line p?

   A m

   B $\frac{m}{2}$

   C $\frac{-m}{2}$

   D -1

2. What is the slope of the line passing through the points $A(-4, -3)$ and $B(-5, -6)$?

   F $\frac{-11}{3}$

   G $\frac{1}{3}$

   H   1

   J   3

3. Line segments connect these four points $A(-6, -9)$, $B(-1,-3)$, $C(9,5)$, $D(4, -2)$ to form a quadrilateral. Which is the most precise name of the figure?

   A   rhombus

   B   trapezoid

   C   parallelogram

   D   square

4. In parallelogram $ABCD$, the coordinates of three of the vertices are $A(-3, -3)$, $B(4, -3)$, and $C(7, 3)$. What are the coordinates of vertex D?

   F   (3, 1)

   G   (1, 3)

   H   (3, 0)

   J   (0, 3)

5. What is the equation of the line which passes through points (−4,3) and (8, −1)?

A $y = \frac{3}{4}x + 5\frac{1}{2}$

B $y = \frac{1}{3}x - \frac{5}{3}$

C $y = \frac{-1}{3}x + \frac{5}{3}$

D $y = \frac{-3}{4}x + 5\frac{1}{2}$

6. What is the equation of the line which has a slope of 0 and passes through point (−5, −6)?

F $y = -6$

G $y = 6$

H $x = -5$

J $x = 5$

SYMMETRY

SOL G.2 *The student will use pictorial representations, including computer software and coordinate methods, to solve problems involving **symmetry** and transformation. This will include investigating and determining whether a figure is symmetric with respect to a line or a point.*

When a figure can be mapped, folded, or rotated onto itself, then it has **symmetry**. Symmetry is found in nature. It is also is a key feature in the artistic designs of many cultures. Most manufactured items have some kind of symmetry, too.

1 A figure can have one or both of two basic symmetries.

- A figure that folds onto itself has **reflectional** symmetry. *Reflectional, line, bilateral,* or *mirror* symmetry are all terms for the same type of symmetry. A figure may have none, one, or more than one line of symmetry.

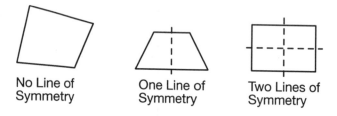

No Line of   One Line of   Two Lines of
Symmetry   Symmetry   Symmetry

- A figure has **rotational** symmetry if there is a rotation of 180° or less that maps the figure onto itself. *Point symmetry* is when a figure has a rotational symmetry of 180°. A figure may have none, one, or more than one rotational symmetry.

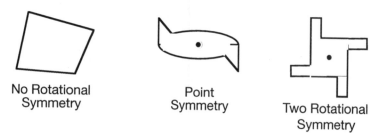

No Rotational   Point
Symmetry   Symmetry   Two Rotational
Symmetry

2 Some polygons have no symmetry. Others have just one. Regular polygons have many symmetries. A square has four reflectional and four rotational symmetries:

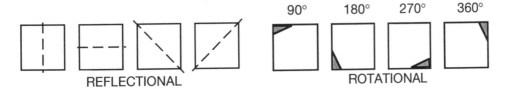

EXAMPLE 1 What kind of symmetry does this figure have?

A reflectional symmetry only

B rotational symmetry only

C both reflectional and rotational symmetry

D no symmetry

Strategy
- You can fold the figure along the line indicated in the diagram at the right, and the halves will match exactly. Therefore, the figure has line symmetry.

- Since the design is based on squares and triangles, and since these figures can have rotational symmetry, all you have to do is rotate the figure 180° to check if the design is the same. It is.

- The figure has both reflectional and rotational symmetry.

Solution Choose C.

What kind of symmetry does this playing card have?

A reflectional symmetry

B rotational symmetry

C reflectional and rotational symmetry

D no symmetry

EXAMPLE 2 Which of these quadrilaterals has rotational but not reflectional symmetry?

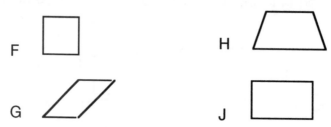

F   H

G   J

Strategy

- Check each figure for both reflectional and rotational symmetry.
- ALL squares (F) have both reflectional and rotational symmetry.
- The parallelogram at G has only rotational symmetry. Spin it 180° and it maps onto itself. But you can't fold it along a line and have the halves match, so it lacks reflectional symmetry.
- You can fold the trapezoid (H) and the rectangle (J) along a line and have the halves match, so both have reflectional symmetry.

Solution   Choose G.

Try It 2

Which quadrilateral has both reflectional and rotational symmetry?

F   a trapezoid

G   a parallelogram

H   a rhombus

J   a kite

EXAMPLE 3 How many lines of symmetry does the following figure have?

A   6

B   4

C   3

D   1

180

Strategy
- The hexagon has a vertical line of symmetry.

- The equilateral triangle has a rotational symmetry of 120°, and the figure makes a complete cycle in 3 rotations. This provides 3 lines of symmetry, as shown in the figure on the right.

Solution   Choose C.

 Try It 3

How many lines of symmetry does the following figure have?

A 2

B 4

C 6

D 8

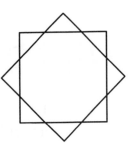

EXAMPLE 4 The image (new position) of *D after* a counterclockwise rotation of 120° about *O* is—

F C

G B

H E

J F

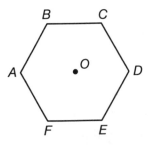

Strategy
- A hexagon has a rotational symmetry of 60°. Since 120° is double this, you are looking for a letter 2 vertices away from D. This eliminates choices F and H.

- A **counterclockwise** rotation goes in the opposite direction from the rotation of the hands on a normal clock. This eliminates choice J , which is the result of a **clockwise** rotation.

Counterclockwise

Solution   Choose G.

Try It 4

The image of *E after* a counterclockwise rotation of 90° about *O* is—

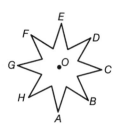

F C

G D

H F

J G

TRY IT! Answers: *1. B   2. H   3. D   4. J*

Sample Virginia SOL Questions

1. Which quadrilateral has both reflectional and rotational symmetry?

   A a kite

   B a trapezoid

   C a parallelogram

   D a rectangle

2. How many lines of symmetry does the following figure have?

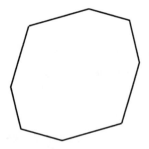

   F 2

   G 3

   H 4

   J 6

3. What kind of symmetry does the following figure have?

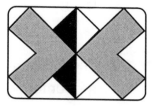

   A reflectional symmetry

   B rotational symmetry

   C reflectional and rotational symmetry

   D no symmetry

4. The image of *E after* a counter-clockwise rotation of 120° about *M* is—

   F A

   G B

   H C

   J K

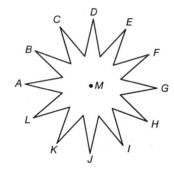

182

TRANSFORMATIONS

SOL G.2 *The student will use pictorial representations, including computer software and coordinate methods, to solve problems involving symmetry and **transformation**. This will include determining whether a figure has been translated, reflected, or rotated.*

REVIEW OF TRANSFORMATIONS

Any time you transform a figure—that is move, shrink or enlarge the figure—you make a **transformation** of that figure.

There are four ways to describe a figure's movement. You can move it by a **flip** (a **reflection**), a **slide** (a **translation**), a **turn** (a **rotation**) or a **change of size** of the figure by scaling it (a **dilation**).

1 A **reflection (flip)** is a transformation where every point is flipped over a line, called a **line of reflection**. Each point of the figure ($\triangle ABC$) (called the **preimage**) and corresponding point of its reflected **image** ($\triangle A'B'C'$) is the same distance from the line. The position and orientation (direction it faces) of the figure changes, but its size does not change.

When a preimage is reflected across the *y*-axis, a vertical line, the *y*-coordinates of the image do not change, **but the x-coordinates become the opposite of what they were in the preimage,** and take the opposite signs. Look at the diagram and make sure you understand how this happens.

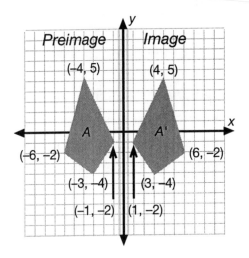

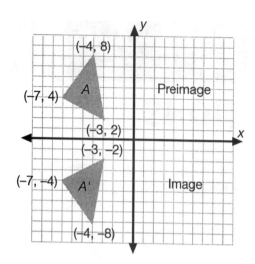

Similarly, when a preimage is reflected across the x-axis, a horizontal line, the x-coordinates of the image do not change, **but the y-coordinates become the opposite of what they were in the preimage.**

2 A **translation (slide)** is a transformation where every point in the figure moves the same distance and in the same direction. A translation maps each preimage point to exactly one image point. During a translation, each x-coordinate changes by the same amount, and each y-coordinate

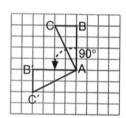

changes by the same amount. Each point in (ABCD) is moved to the right 4 points and down 3 points to form the image (A´B´C´D´). Only the position of the figure changes. Its size and orientation do not change.

3 A **rotation (turn)** is a transformation where a figure turns (clockwise or counterclockwise) around a fixed point, called the **point of rotation.** The point of rotation doesn't have to be on the figure. The figure's position and orientation change, but its size does not. The figure △ABC on the right was moved counterclockwise 90° to form its image △A´B´C´.

Rotations, reflections, and translations are examples of **isometries**—that is, congruent transformations. They produce images that are congruent to their preimages. The next transformation—dilation—is NOT an isometry. It does not produce an image congruent to the preimage.

4 A **dilation** is when a figure is enlarged or reduced (**scaled**) in size, which produces an image that is similar to, but not congruent to, its preimage. The orientation of the figure does not change.

- The amount a figure is enlarged or reduced is called its **scale factor**. This is the ratio between the size of the figure (preimage) and its image.

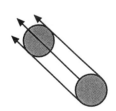 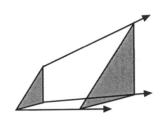 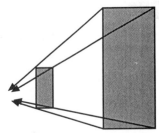

Scale factor of 1:1 congruency   Scale factor of 2:1 or 2   Scale factor of 1:3 or $\frac{1}{3}$

- Dilations that form a congruent image are called **identity dilations**, and have a scale factor of 1.

- Dilations that make objects **larger** have a scale factor **greater than 1**. (For example, a scale factor of 2:1—or simply, 2—means that the image is twice the size of the original.)

- Dilations that make objects **smaller** have a scale factor **less than 1**. (For example, a scale factor of 1:3 or $\frac{1}{3}$ means that the image is one-third the size of the original.)

EXAMPLE 1 Which of the following best describes the tranformation shown in the following graph?

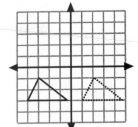

    A   translation, $(x, y) \rightarrow (x + 5, y)$
    B   reflection, $(x, y) \rightarrow (-x, y)$
    C   reflection, $(x, y) \rightarrow (x, -y)$
    D   translation, $(x, y) \rightarrow (x - 5, y)$

Strategy

- Remember that a reflection (flip) changes a figure's orientation. Since this figure's orientation is not changed, choices B and C are eliminated.

- The image is 5 spaces to the right of the preimage. This means that 5 was added to each *x*-value of the preimage.

- Choose A, because it shows 5 added to the *x*-value.

Solution   Choose A.

 Try It 1   Which of the following best describes the tranformation shown in the following graph?

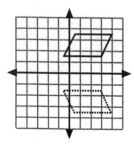

A   reflection, $(x, y) \rightarrow (-x, y)$

B   translation, $(x, y) \rightarrow (x - 5, y)$

C   reflection, $(x, y) \rightarrow (x, -y)$

D   translation, $(x, y) \rightarrow (x, y - 5)$

EXAMPLE 2 Which of the images is a 90° clockwise rotation of the shaded preimage about the point (2, 3)?

F   *f*

G   *g*

H   *h*

J   *j*

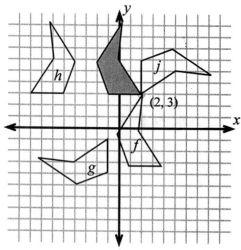

Strategy   • Since the shaded preimage includes point (2, 3), the rotated image will also include this point. Choices G and H do not include this point and can be eliminated.

186

- The orientation of Choice F is the same as the shaded figure. It is a translation (slide) and therefore can be eliminated.

- Choice J is a 90° clockwise rotation.

Solution   Choose J.

Try It 2

Which of these images is a 60° rotation of the shaded preimage about the point (–2, –6)?

F   *f*
G   *g*
H   *h*
J   *j*

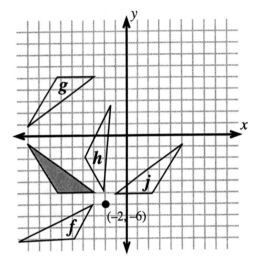

EXAMPLE 3 Which of the following shows a figure reflected about the *y*-axis?

A

B

C

D

Strategy

- Remember that a reflection (flip) changes orientation. Just think of looking at words in a mirror. You can eliminate choices B and D because the orientation has not changed.

- Choice A shows a change in orientation, but you can eliminate it because it is a rotation and not a reflection.

- Choice C shows a change in orientation, and the foot is flipped so that in both the image and the preimage the heel is closest to the *y*-axis.

Solution   Choose C.

Try It 3   Which of the following is an example of a reflection of the figure in the box?

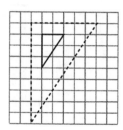

A

B

C

D

EXAMPLE 4 The dotted triangle is the image of the solid triangle. What is the scale factor?

F $\frac{1}{3}$

G $\frac{1}{2}$

H 3

J 4

Strategy

- A figure's size is changed by multiplying each side by the scale factor. If you use a scale factor less than one (fraction or decimal), you get a smaller figure. Since the dotted triangle is larger, it eliminates choices F and G.

- Compare the length of one corresponding side of both triangles as a ratio. The smaller figure has a side of 2 (the "top" side), and the larger triangle has a corresponding side of 6:

$$\frac{\text{larger}}{\text{smaller}} = \frac{6}{2} = 3 \text{ or } \frac{9}{3} = 3$$

Solution: Choose H.

Try It 4

Figure $A'B'C'D'$ is the image of figure $ABCD$. Which is the scale factor?

F $\frac{1}{4}$

G $\frac{1}{3}$

H   3

J   –3

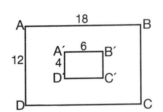

EXAMPLE 5 On a chess board, a playing piece, a knight, starts at (2,3). It moves two spaces up vertically and one horizontally to the right. What are the coordinates of the knight's new position?

A   (0,4)

B   (1,5)

C   (3,5)

D   (4,4)

Strategy

- Ordered pairs have x first, then y. The x-value determines the left-right position, and the y-value determines the vertical position. (Note that the problem gives the knight's x-move second and its y-move first!)

- Add the 1 move to the right to the x-value and the 2 spaces upward to the y-value of the ordered pair: (2 + 1, 3 + 2) → (3,5).

Solution: Choose C.

At a half-time show, a marching band moved in formation. The lead drummer started at a point with coordinates (-4,–2) and moved 5 steps up and 4 steps right. What are the coordinates of the drummer's final position?

A (1,2)
B (1,3)
C (0,3)
D (0,–6)

EXAMPLE 6 Which is the translation rule for the translation of point P(8,5) to point P′(3,8)?

F $(x, y) \rightarrow (x - 5, y + 3)$

G $(x, y) \rightarrow (x - 5, y - 3)$

H $(x, y) \rightarrow (x + 5, y + 3)$

J $(x, y) \rightarrow (x + 5, y - 3)$

Strategy
- The first point's x-value changes from 8 to 3—a decrease of 5 (or, mathematically, minus 5). This eliminates choices H and J since they add 5.

- The y-value, the second term of each ordered pair, changes from 5 to 8—that is an increase of 3 (or add 3). This eliminates choice G.

Solution: Choose F, since it meets the described changes in both x and y.

Try It 6

Which is the translation rule for the translation of point A(−3,1) to point A′(−8,7)?

F $(x, y) \rightarrow (x - 6, y + 5)$

G $(x, y) \rightarrow (x + 5, y - 6)$

H $(x, y) \rightarrow (x - 11, y + 6)$

J $(x, y) \rightarrow (x - 5, y + 6)$

EXAMPLE 7 The negative of a 35-mm roll of film is 1 in. by 1.5 in. Which of these common print sizes is a dilation of a 35-mm negative?

    A 3 in. by 5 in.

    B 4 in. by 6 in.

    C 5 in. by 7 in.

    D 8 in. by 10 in.

Strategy
- To determine if one figure is a dilation of another, find the ratios of the corresponding dimensions. If the ratios are same, then you have a dilation.

- Set up ratios comparing the answer choices and the film negative.
  - Choice A, $\frac{3}{1} = 3$ and $\frac{5}{1.5} = 3\frac{1}{3}$ are not equal ratios; therefore, this is not a dilation.
  - Choice B, $\frac{4}{1} = 4$ and $\frac{6}{1.5} = 4$ <u>are</u> equal ratios. Therefore this <u>is</u> a dilation.

Solution: Choose B.

Try It 7

The sides of a right triangle are 24 cm, 32 cm, and 40 cm. Which of the following is a dilation of this triangle?

    A 5 cm, 12 cm, 13 cm

    B 8 cm, 15 cm, 17 cm

    C 12 cm, 16 cm, 20 cm

    D 8 cm, 24 cm, 25 cm

EXAMPLE 8 Rectangle *GHJK* is rotated 90° clockwise about point *O* to produce the image rectangle *ABCD*. What is the pre-image of point *A*?

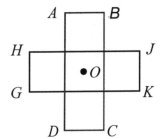

    F point K

    G point G

    H point H

    J point J

Strategy

- Since *GHJK* is rotated 90° clockwise, points J and K are the preimage points of C and D. This eliminates choices F and J.

- Rectangles *GHJK* and *ABCD* are congruent. You know that the order of the letters (points) in the image corresponds to the order in the preimage. Therefore, the point corresponding to A is G.

Solution: Choose G.

Try It 8

Rectangle *GHJK* is rotated 90° clockwise about point O. The image is rectangle *ABCD*. What is the image of $\overline{HJ}$?

F $\overline{BC}$

G $\overline{AD}$

H $\overline{AB}$

J $\overline{DC}$

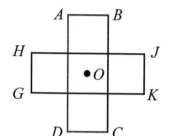

EXAMPLE 9 What are the coordinates of the image of △*SUD* under the translation $\langle 4, -5 \rangle$?

$$\begin{array}{c} \begin{array}{ccc} S & U & D \end{array} \\ \begin{array}{c} x \\ y \end{array}\begin{bmatrix} -1 & 2 & 3 \\ -1 & -5 & 2 \end{bmatrix} \end{array}$$

A $\begin{bmatrix} 3 & 7 & 6 \\ -6 & -3 & -10 \end{bmatrix}$

B $\begin{bmatrix} -6 & -3 & -2 \\ 3 & -1 & 6 \end{bmatrix}$

C $\begin{bmatrix} -6 & -2 & -3 \\ 3 & 6 & -1 \end{bmatrix}$

D $\begin{bmatrix} 3 & 6 & 7 \\ -6 & -10 & -3 \end{bmatrix}$

192

Strategy

- To find the vertices of the image, you add a 2 by 3 translation matrix to the matrix of the vertices of the preimage.

Vertices of Preimage   Translation Matrix   Vertices of Image

$$\begin{bmatrix} -1 & 2 & 3 \\ -1 & -5 & 2 \end{bmatrix} + \begin{bmatrix} 4 & 4 & 4 \\ -5 & -5 & -5 \end{bmatrix} = \begin{bmatrix} 3 & 6 & 7 \\ -6 & -10 & -3 \end{bmatrix}$$

Solution: Choose D.

Try It 9

What are the coordinates of the image of $\triangle ABC$ under the translation $\langle -3,5 \rangle$?

$$\begin{matrix} A & B & C \end{matrix}$$
$$\begin{bmatrix} -5 & -2 & -8 \\ 7 & 2 & 3 \end{bmatrix}$$

A $\begin{bmatrix} 12 & 7 & 8 \\ -8 & -11 & -5 \end{bmatrix}$

B $\begin{bmatrix} -8 & -11 & -5 \\ 12 & 8 & 7 \end{bmatrix}$

C $\begin{bmatrix} -8 & -5 & -11 \\ 12 & 7 & 8 \end{bmatrix}$

D $\begin{bmatrix} 12 & 8 & 7 \\ -8 & -5 & -11 \end{bmatrix}$

EXAMPLE 10 Which pair of transformations has been performed on preimage A to get image A`, using the 2 intersecting lines shown?

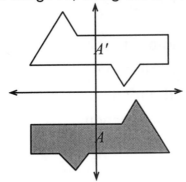

193

F   a translation and a 90° rotation

G   two reflections

H   two 90° rotations

J   a reflection and a translation

Strategy

- A rotation of 90° is a $\frac{1}{4}$ turn, and the image (A') is turned more than that, so choice F is eliminated.

- Two reflections are the equivalent of one translation. A translation does not change orientation. But the image has a changed orientation, so Choice G can be eliminated.

- Two rotations of 90° would leave the figure's orientation upside down. This eliminates choice H.

- The image A' is moved up from A (translated) and is also flipped (reflected) over the y-axis.

Solution: Choose J.

Try It 10

Which pair of transformation has been performed on preimage A to get image A´ using the 2 intersecting lines shown?

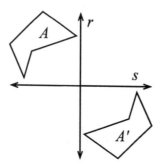

F   a translation and a reflection

G   a rotation and a reflection

H   a translation and a rotation

J   a reflection and a reflection

TRY IT Answers: *1. C*   *2. H*   *3. B*   *4. G*   *5. C*   *6. J*   *7. C*   *8. F*   *9. C*   *10. J*

1. Which of the images is a 60° clockwise rotation about the point (–2, 1) of the shaded preimage?

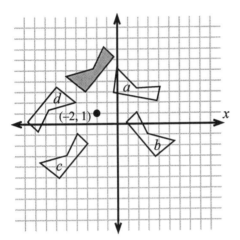

A   a
B   b
C   c
D   d

2. Which are the coordinates of the translation of △ABC using the rule (x, y) → (x + 1, y – 2)?

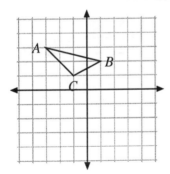

F   A(–2, 1), B(1, 0), C(0, –1)
G   A(–2, 1), B(2, 0), C(0, –1)
H   A(2, –1), B(2, 4), C(2, –3)
J   A(2, 1), B(1, 4), C(2, –3)

3. At an amusement park, Andy gets on a Ferris wheel at ground level. What rotation of the wheel puts Andy at the top of the Ferris wheel?

A   45°
B   90°
C   180°
D   270°

4. Which pair of transformations has been applied to preimage A to result in image A´?

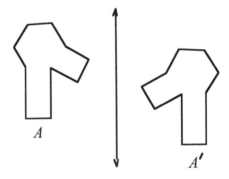

F   translation and rotation
G   reflection and reflection
H   rotation and reflection
J   reflection and translation

5. Deborah transformed △BAC to △SAT using a dilation. Which scale factor did she use?

A   3
B   2
C $1\frac{1}{2}$
D $\frac{1}{3}$

195

6. △RSO is rotated 180° clockwise around point O. What is the new location of point R?

F M
G N
H P
J Q

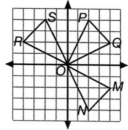

7. Brian puts a dot of paint on the right hand side of a piece of paper and then folds it. When he opens it there are two figures 1 on the right and 1 on the left. Which transformation was performed?

A a rotation
B a translation
C a dilation
D a reflection

8. A translation maps the point (2, 5) onto the point (6,–1). What is the image of the point (3,–1) under the same translation?

F (7,–7)
G (7,–5)
H (–1,–6)
J (–1,–5)

9. What are the coordinates of the image of △BAT under the translation ⟨–9,4⟩?

$$\begin{array}{ccc} B & A & T \end{array}$$
$$\begin{bmatrix} 7 & -8 & 0 \\ 2 & 5 & -6 \end{bmatrix}$$

A $\begin{bmatrix} -2 & -17 & -9 \\ 6 & 9 & -2 \end{bmatrix}$

B $\begin{bmatrix} -2 & -9 & -17 \\ 6 & -2 & 9 \end{bmatrix}$

C $\begin{bmatrix} 6 & 9 & -2 \\ -2 & -17 & -9 \end{bmatrix}$

D $\begin{bmatrix} 6 & -2 & 9 \\ -2 & -2 & -17 \end{bmatrix}$

10. Which group of coordinate pairs names the vertex points of the image of the triangle when it has been reflected across the x-axis?

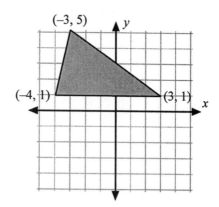

F (3, 5), (3, –1), (–4, –1)
G (–3, –5), (3, –1), (–4, –1)
H (–3, –5), (3, 1), (–4, –1)
J (3, 5), (–3, 1), (4, 1)

VECTORS

SOL G.15 *The student will—*
*   *draw a system of vectors and find the resultant graphically, write the components of a vector as a column matrix, and find the resultant by matrix addition.*
*   *solve practical problems using a system of vectors.*

1 **Vectors** are measures that have both **magnitude** (size) and **direction**. There are three ways to describe a vector:

*   Naming both the magnitude and the direction. For example, the magnitude of a vector AB (written $\overrightarrow{AB}$) might be 51 and its direction northwest (45° north of west).

*   Using an ordered-pair notation to describe $\overrightarrow{AB}$, where the *x*-value represents the horizontal change from *A* to *B* and the *y*-value represents the vertical change. This is somewhat similar to describing a vector in terms of its slope.

*   Using a **column matrix** for representing the vector (*x*, *y*), with the *x*-value placed above the *y*-value: $\begin{bmatrix} x \\ y \end{bmatrix}$ This is a form that makes operations with vectors easier.

2 Here are three basic rules for working with vectors.

*   Two vectors are equal if and only if they are equal in **both** magnitude and direction.

*   If $\overrightarrow{c}$ is a vector, then $-\overrightarrow{c}$ s defined as having the same magnitude but the reverse direction to $\overrightarrow{c}$. Subtracting $\overrightarrow{c}$ is the same as adding $-\overrightarrow{c}$.

*   Multiplying a vector by a number or **scalar** only has the effect of changing its magnitude. It does not change its direction.

197

3 The sum or difference of two or more vectors is called the **resultant**.

There are two methods for finding the resultant of two vectors, the **head-to-tail** method and the **parallelogram** method.

- When you add vectors using the **head-to-tail** method, one vector slides along the other until its "tail" meets the "head" of the second vector. (In the diagrams below, notice how $\vec{b}$ slides along the line of $\vec{a}$.) The resultant is the line connecting the tail of $\vec{a}$ to the head of $\vec{b}$.

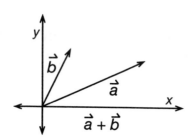

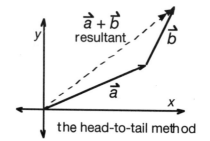

the head-to-tail method

- In the **parallelogram** method, you sketch the 2 missing sides of a parallelogram. The resultant is the diagonal of the parallelogram.

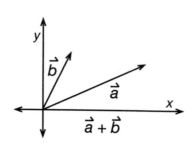

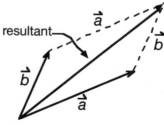

the parallelogram method

EXAMPLE 1 Which of the following is the correct column matrix for representing the vector (4, –1)?

A. $\begin{bmatrix} -4 \\ 1 \end{bmatrix}$
C. $\begin{bmatrix} 4 \\ 1 \end{bmatrix}$

B. $\begin{bmatrix} 4 \\ -1 \end{bmatrix}$
D. $\begin{bmatrix} -1 \\ 4 \end{bmatrix}$

Strategy
- The easiest way to change an ordered pair into a column matrix is to take the *x*-value and place it above the *y*-value.

198

- The ordered pair is (4, –1). The *x*-value is 4, and the *y*-value is –1.

  So the column matrix is 4 over –1, or $\begin{bmatrix} 4 \\ -1 \end{bmatrix}$.

Solution   Choose B.

Try It 1

Which of the following is the correct column matrix for representing the vector (–3, –7)?

A $\begin{bmatrix} 3 \\ -7 \end{bmatrix}$ C $\begin{bmatrix} -7 \\ -3 \end{bmatrix}$

B $\begin{bmatrix} -3 \\ -7 \end{bmatrix}$ D $\begin{bmatrix} 7 \\ -3 \end{bmatrix}$

EXAMPLE 2 An airplane is flying on a northwest heading at an air speed of 200 mi/hr ($\vec{v}$). The wind is blowing from the east at 50 mi/hr ($\vec{u}$). Which graph shows the actual course and ground speed ($\vec{r}$)?

F 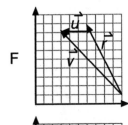   G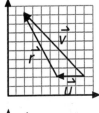

H 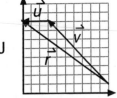   J

Strategy

- Since the wind ($\vec{u}$) is from the east, this vector will be horizontal. This eliminates choice H, which shows the wind blowing from the southeast.

- When adding vectors, it does not matter which vector you add first.

- One method of adding vectors is placing them head to tail. You can eliminate choices that do not place $\vec{v}$ and $\vec{u}$ head to tail. This eliminates choices F (head to head) and G (tail to tail).

199

Solution   Choose J.

Try It 2   Add vectors $\vec{u}$ (3 southwest) and $\vec{v}$ (4 west) Which graph shows the resultant, $\vec{r}$?

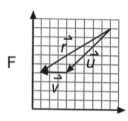

F

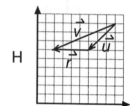

H

G

J

4 In subtraction, unlike addition, it DOES matter which vector you start with. To subtract a vector $\vec{b}$ from a vector $\vec{a}$, you **add** the vector **opposite** to b. That is, you add a vector that has the same magnitude as $\vec{b}$ but whose direction is opposite to $\vec{b}$.

To do this, take $\vec{b}$ and change its direction to $\vec{b}'$ by rotating it 180° around its tail. (You do not change the direction of $\vec{a}$.) Look at the diagram:

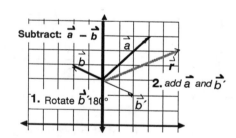

Now you can add $\vec{a}$ and $\vec{b}'$ in the usual way, as the diagram shows.

EXAMPLE 3 Subtract $\vec{v}$ from $\vec{u}$. Which graph shows the correct resultant, $\vec{r}$?

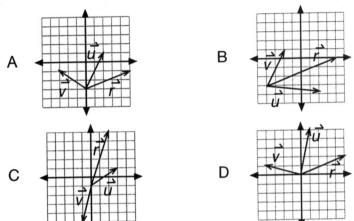

Strategy

- To subtract $\vec{v}$ from $\vec{u}$, add the vector opposite to $\vec{v}$—that is, one pointing in the opposite direction. Take $\vec{v}$ and change its direction by rotating it 180°. Remember, **you do not change the direction of $\vec{u}$.**

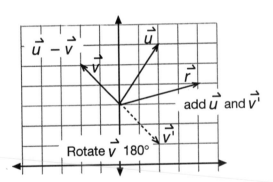

- Now you can add the vectors, using the head-to-tail method.

- The only diagram that shows the resultant in the correct position after the addition is A.

Solution Choose A.

Try It 3 → Subtract $\vec{u}$ from $\vec{v}$. Which graph shows the resultant, $\vec{r}$?

A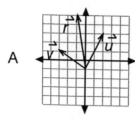

B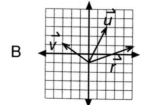

C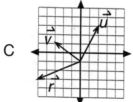

D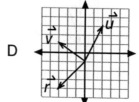

EXAMPLE 4 If $\vec{u} = \begin{bmatrix} 2 \\ 5 \end{bmatrix}$ and $\vec{v} = \begin{bmatrix} 3 \\ -1 \end{bmatrix}$, what is $\vec{u} + 2\vec{v}$?

F $\begin{bmatrix} 8 \\ 3 \end{bmatrix}$

G $\begin{bmatrix} 5 \\ 2 \end{bmatrix}$

H $\begin{bmatrix} 6 \\ -3 \end{bmatrix}$

J $\begin{bmatrix} 8 \\ 7 \end{bmatrix}$

Strategy

- First, what is being asked is the same as adding three matrices, $\vec{u} + \vec{v} + \vec{v}$. When adding or subtracting matrices you add or subtract the corresponding terms.

$$\begin{bmatrix} 2 \\ 5 \end{bmatrix} + \begin{bmatrix} 3 \\ -1 \end{bmatrix} + \begin{bmatrix} 3 \\ -1 \end{bmatrix} = \begin{bmatrix} 2+3+3 \\ 5-1-1 \end{bmatrix} = \begin{bmatrix} 8 \\ 3 \end{bmatrix}$$

Solution

Choose F.

202

If $\vec{u} = \begin{bmatrix} -2 \\ 3 \end{bmatrix}$ and $\vec{v} = \begin{bmatrix} 4 \\ 0 \end{bmatrix}$, what is $2\vec{u} + 3\vec{v}$?

F $\begin{bmatrix} 8 \\ 6 \end{bmatrix}$ G $\begin{bmatrix} 2 \\ 6 \end{bmatrix}$

H $\begin{bmatrix} 4 \\ 6 \end{bmatrix}$ J $\begin{bmatrix} 16 \\ 6 \end{bmatrix}$

EXAMPLE 5 Which column matrix represents the resultant vector for the sum of $\vec{u}$ and $\vec{v}$ in the graph below?

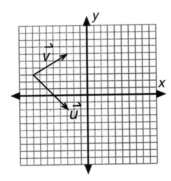

A $\begin{bmatrix} 2 \\ 1 \end{bmatrix}$ B $\begin{bmatrix} 10 \\ 2 \end{bmatrix}$

C $\begin{bmatrix} -10 \\ 2 \end{bmatrix}$ D $\begin{bmatrix} 10 \\ -2 \end{bmatrix}$

Strategy

- Remember that a column matrix represents the change in the horizontal (*x*-value) and the change in the vertical (*y*-value) of a vector. This represents the change in magnitude.

- Find the resultant using the head-to-tail method.

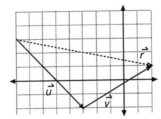

- The vectors start at point (–8,3) and their resultant (sum) ends at point (2,1).

- To find the *x*-value of the change in magnitude you set up an equation:

  Initial *x*-coordinate + change = endpoint *x*-coordinate
  Substitute values and simplify: $-8 + c = 2 \rightarrow c = 10$

- To find the *y*-value of the change in magnitude you setup an equation:

  Initial *y*-coordinate + change = endpoint *y*-coordinate
  Substitute values and simplify: $3 + d = 1 \rightarrow d = -2$

- The resultant is (10, –2).

Solution   Choose D.

Try It 5   Which column matrix represents the resultant vector for the sum of $\vec{u}$ and $\vec{v}$ in the graph below?

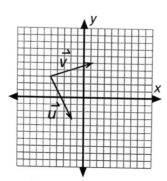

A $\begin{bmatrix} 4 \\ -1 \end{bmatrix}$ 　　　　　 B $\begin{bmatrix} 9 \\ -4 \end{bmatrix}$

C $\begin{bmatrix} -9 \\ -4 \end{bmatrix}$ 　　　　　 D $\begin{bmatrix} -9 \\ 4 \end{bmatrix}$

EXAMPLE 6 A pigeon is flying west at 12 mi/hr. There is a 17 mi/hr wind blowing due north. What is the actual flight speed of the pigeon?

F   43.3 mi/hr

G 20.8 mi/hr

H 12 mi/hr

J   5.39 mi/hr

Strategy

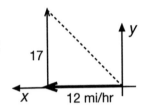

- First, draw a pair a vectors representing the pigeon and the wind. Next, draw the resultant vector (dotted line).

- The actual speed can be found using the Pythagorean Theorem:

speed $= \sqrt{12^2 + 17^2} \rightarrow \sqrt{144 + 289} \rightarrow \sqrt{433} \approx 20.8$ mi/hr

Solution   Choose G.

Try It 6   A plane is flying due south at 200 mi/hr. The wind is blowing east at 30 mi/hr. What is the actual speed at which the plane is flying, to the nearest mile per hour?

F   230 mi/hr

G 205 mi/hr

H 202 mi/hr

J   201 mi/hr

TRY IT Answers: 1. B   2. G   3. C   4. F   5. B   6. G

1. Add $\vec{u}$ and $\vec{v}$. Which graph shows the resultant, $\vec{r}$?

A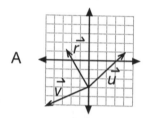

B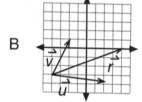

C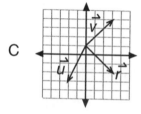

D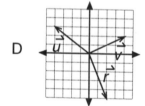

2. A football player runs a pass pattern of 16 yds. straight up the field and then 12 yds. to the right sideline. Using vector addition, what is the actual distance from starting point to ending point ?

   F 20 yd

   G 24 yd

   H 28 yd

   J 32 yd

3. If $\vec{u} = \begin{bmatrix} 2 \\ 5 \end{bmatrix}$ and $\vec{v} = \begin{bmatrix} 8 \\ -1 \end{bmatrix}$. What is the correct column matrix for $2\vec{u} + \vec{v}$?

   A $\begin{bmatrix} 5 \\ 3 \end{bmatrix}$

   B $\begin{bmatrix} 7 \\ 3 \end{bmatrix}$

   C $\begin{bmatrix} 12 \\ 9 \end{bmatrix}$

   D $\begin{bmatrix} 8 \\ 11 \end{bmatrix}$

4. Which of the following is the correct column matrix for representing the vector (–5,8)?

F $\begin{bmatrix} 5 \\ 8 \end{bmatrix}$

G $\begin{bmatrix} 5 \\ -8 \end{bmatrix}$

H $\begin{bmatrix} -5 \\ 8 \end{bmatrix}$

J $\begin{bmatrix} 8 \\ -5 \end{bmatrix}$

5. Subtract $\vec{u}$ from $\vec{v}$. Which graph shows the resultant, $\vec{r}$?

A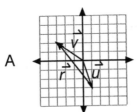

B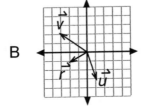

C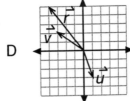

D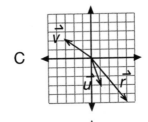

Answer Sheet for Practice SOL Geometry Test

Lines and Angles

1. Ⓐ Ⓑ Ⓒ Ⓓ
2. Ⓕ Ⓖ Ⓗ Ⓙ
3. Ⓐ Ⓑ Ⓒ Ⓓ
4. Ⓕ Ⓖ Ⓗ Ⓙ
5. Ⓐ Ⓑ Ⓒ Ⓓ
6. Ⓕ Ⓖ Ⓗ Ⓙ
7. Ⓐ Ⓑ Ⓒ Ⓓ
8. Ⓕ Ⓖ Ⓗ Ⓙ
9. Ⓐ Ⓑ Ⓒ Ⓓ
10. Ⓕ Ⓖ Ⓗ Ⓙ
11. Ⓐ Ⓑ Ⓒ Ⓓ

Logic and Triangles

12. Ⓕ Ⓖ Ⓗ Ⓙ
13. Ⓐ Ⓑ Ⓒ Ⓓ
14. Ⓕ Ⓖ Ⓗ Ⓙ
15. Ⓐ Ⓑ Ⓒ Ⓓ
16. Ⓕ Ⓖ Ⓗ Ⓙ
17. Ⓐ Ⓑ Ⓒ Ⓓ
18. Ⓕ Ⓖ Ⓗ Ⓙ
19. Ⓐ Ⓑ Ⓒ Ⓓ
20. Ⓕ Ⓖ Ⓗ Ⓙ

21. Ⓐ Ⓑ Ⓒ Ⓓ
22. Ⓕ Ⓖ Ⓗ Ⓙ
23. Ⓐ Ⓑ Ⓒ Ⓓ

Polygons and Circles

24. Ⓕ Ⓖ Ⓗ Ⓙ
25. Ⓐ Ⓑ Ⓒ Ⓓ
26. Ⓕ Ⓖ Ⓗ Ⓙ
27. Ⓐ Ⓑ Ⓒ Ⓓ
28. Ⓕ Ⓖ Ⓗ Ⓙ
29. Ⓐ Ⓑ Ⓒ Ⓓ
30. Ⓕ Ⓖ Ⓗ Ⓙ
31. Ⓐ Ⓑ Ⓒ Ⓓ
32. Ⓕ Ⓖ Ⓗ Ⓙ
33. Ⓐ Ⓑ Ⓒ Ⓓ

Three-Dimensional Figures

34. Ⓕ Ⓖ Ⓗ Ⓙ
35. Ⓐ Ⓑ Ⓒ Ⓓ
36. Ⓕ Ⓖ Ⓗ Ⓙ
37. Ⓐ Ⓑ Ⓒ Ⓓ

Proportional Reasoning

38. Ⓕ Ⓖ Ⓗ Ⓙ
39. Ⓐ Ⓑ Ⓒ Ⓓ

Coordinate Relations, Transformations, and Vectors

40. Ⓕ Ⓖ Ⓗ Ⓙ
41. Ⓐ Ⓑ Ⓒ Ⓓ
42. Ⓕ Ⓖ Ⓗ Ⓙ
43. Ⓐ Ⓑ Ⓒ Ⓓ
44. Ⓕ Ⓖ Ⓗ Ⓙ
45. Ⓐ Ⓑ Ⓒ Ⓓ

LINES AND ANGLES
(G.3, G.4, G.11)

1. What is the measure of the complement of $\angle ACE$?

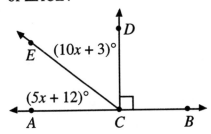

A   63°

B   53°

C   37°

D   15°

2. The measure of $\angle ABG = 110°$. What is the measure of $\angle GBD$?

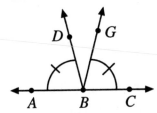

F   20°

G   30°

H   40°

J   75°

3. Kate cuts a piece of metal in the form of a regular polygon (see figure below). At what angle must she cut along adjacent edges of one piece?

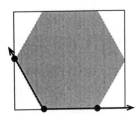

A   60°

B   120°

C   130°

D   240°

4. Use the figure below. Line m is parallel to the base of the triangle? What is the measure of $\angle A$?

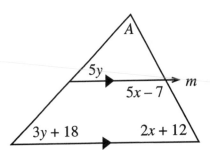

F   73°

G   62°

H   45°

J   25°

5. Which pair of linear equations represents two lines that are perpendicular?

A $y = \frac{-1}{3}x - 1,\ y = -3x + 5$

B $y = x + 1,\ y = x - 1$

C $y = 4x,\ y = \frac{-1}{4}x$

D $y = 4x + 1,\ y = \frac{1}{4}x + 1$

6. Given: $y = 2x + 4$, P(2, 3). Which equation of a line is parallel to the given line and passes through the given point?

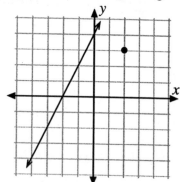

F $y = -2x - 1$

G $y = 2x - 1$

H $y = \frac{1}{2}x - 1$

J $y = \frac{-1}{2}x - 1$

7. Points A(2, –5) and B(–4, 7) are on $\overleftrightarrow{AB}$. Which line is parallel to line $\overleftrightarrow{AB}$?

A $y = \frac{1}{2}x + 7$

B $y = 2x + 7$

C $y = \frac{-1}{2}x + 7$

D $y = -2x + 7$

8. Lines p and m are cut by transversal t. What value of x makes $p \parallel m$?

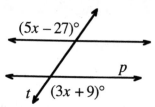

F 9

G 18

H 27

J 36

9. Construct a perpendicular line from $\overline{AB}$ to point E. Which point on $\overleftrightarrow{AB}$ is on the perpendicular?

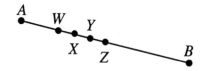

A W

B X

C Y

D Z

10. Construct a perpendicular line at point X on $\overline{AB}$. Which point lies on the perpendicular to $\overline{AB}$?

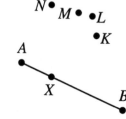

F K

G L

H M

J N

210

11. Given triangle $\angle ABC$, construct an angle bisector of $\angle ABC$. Which point lies on the angle bisector of $\angle ABC$?

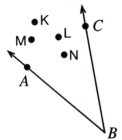

A   K

B   L

C   M

D   N

LOGIC and TRIANGLES
(G.1, G.5, G.6, G.7)

12. Which of the following Venn diagrams illustrates that the reasoning below in **NOT** valid?

All teachers (T) are rich (R). Some rich people are bald (B). Therefore, no teacher is bald.

F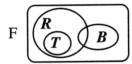

G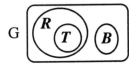

H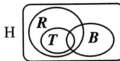

J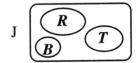

13. Which is the concluding statement for the following chain of reasoning?

$$\sim p \Rightarrow q$$
$$r \Rightarrow \sim q$$
$$s \Rightarrow r$$

A $r \Rightarrow p$

B $s \Rightarrow p$

C $r \Rightarrow q$

D $s \Rightarrow q$

14. Which of the following statements is true about the two triangles below?

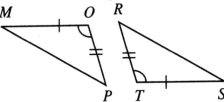

F $\triangle MOP \cong \triangle RST$ by SSS

G $\triangle POM \cong \triangle STR$ by SAS

H $\triangle MOP \cong \triangle STR$ by SAS

J $\triangle MPO \cong \triangle SRT$ by ASA

15. Which correctly completes the statement? To prove $\triangle ABC \cong \triangle XYZ$ by ASA, you must show that $\angle B \cong$ ___ , $\overline{BC} \cong$ ___ , and $\angle C \cong$ ___.

A $\angle Y$, $\overline{XY}$, $\angle X$

B $\angle X$, $\overline{YZ}$, $\angle Z$

C $\angle Y$, $\overline{XZ}$, $\angle X$

D $\angle Y$, $\overline{YZ}$, $\angle Z$

16. In the diagram below, $\overline{AB} \parallel \overline{CD}$, $\angle B \cong \angle D$, and $\overline{AB} \cong \overline{CD}$. What postulate or theorem would prove $\triangle ABF \cong \triangle CDE$?

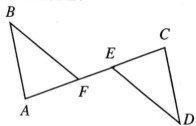

F   SSS

G   SAS

H   ASA

J   AAS

17. Given $\triangle DEF$ and $\overline{AB} \parallel \overline{DE}$, what is the value of x?

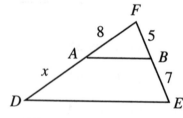

A $\dfrac{35}{8}$

B $\dfrac{56}{5}$

C $\dfrac{40}{7}$

D   10

18. Given: $\overline{AD} \parallel \overline{BC}$, and $\overline{AB}$ and $\overline{DC}$ intersect at point X. Which of the following statements is true?

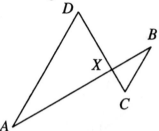

F $\triangle AXD \sim \triangle BXC$ by AA

G $\triangle AXD$ is not similar to $\triangle BXC$

H $\triangle AXD \sim \triangle BXC$ by SAS

J $\triangle AXD \sim \triangle BXC$ by SSS

19. In the diagram below, which is the shortest side?

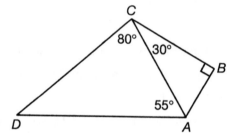

A $\overline{AC}$

B $\overline{AD}$

C $\overline{AB}$

D $\overline{DC}$

20. Use the diagram below. Which of the following values represents the distance $\overline{AC}$ to the nearest tenth of a unit?

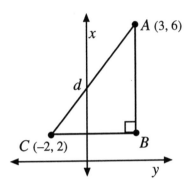

F   4.1
G   6.4
H   8.1
J   9.4

21. Zack placed stakes in the ground to mark the corners of his new pool. He knows the foundation is a parallelogram. Which of the following dimensions makes the pool rectangular?

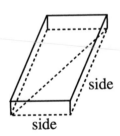

A   Sides: 12 ft and 24 ft; diagonal 26.3 ft
B   Sides: 14 ft and 28 ft; diagonal 31.8 ft
C   Sides: 16 ft and 32 ft; diagonal 35.8 ft
D   Sides: 20 ft and 40 ft; diagonal 43.7 ft

22. A 28 foot ladder leans against a house and the angle it makes with the ground is 60°. To the nearest tenth of a foot, how far up the side of the house does the ladder reach?

F   14.0 ft.
G   19.8 ft.
H   22.5 ft.
J   24.2 ft.

23. Use the diagram below. Billy is flying a kite. To the nearest tenth of a foot, how high is his kite?

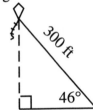

A   208.4 ft.
B   215.8 ft.
C   231.4 ft.
D   310.7 ft.

POLYGONS AND CIRCLES
(G.8, G.9, G.10)

24. What are the values for *x* and *y* in the figure below?

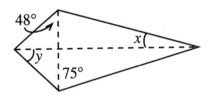

F $x = 42°$ and $y = 15°$
G $x = 52°$ and $y = 30°$
H $x = 15°$ and $y = 42°$
J $x = 30°$ and $y = 52°$

25. What are the coordinates for point D so that $ABCD$ is a parallelogram?

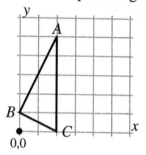

A $D\,(4, 4)$

B $D\,(4, 5)$

C $D\,(5, 4)$

D $D\,(5, 5)$

26. Given the perimeter of the figure below is 64, what are the values for each variable, a and x?

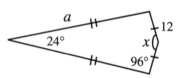

F $a = 26$ $x = 144°$

G $a = 20$ $x = 144°$

H $a = 20$ $x = 60°$

J $a = 40$ $x = 240°$

27. A regular hexagonal mirror is to be framed in wood. At what angles a and b should the wood be cut?

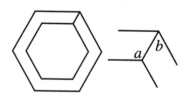

A $a = 120°, b = 60°$

B $a = 60°, b = 120°$

C $a = 60°, b = 60°$

D $a = 120°, b = 120°$

28. The line ℓ is a line of symmetry for the figure $ABCDE$. What is the measure of $\angle EAB$?

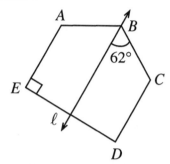

F $59°$

G $108°$

H $118°$

J $236°$

29. In the diagram below, $\overline{AB}$ is a diameter. What is the measure of $\overset{\frown}{DA}$ if $m\overset{\frown}{BD} = 125°$?

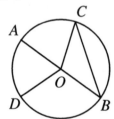

A $235°$

B $65°$

C $55°$

D $45°$

214

30. In the diagram below, what is the measure of ∠RPU?

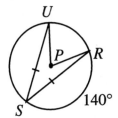

F   40°
G   70°
H   80°
J   20°

31. Given: m∠BKD = 100° and m$\widehat{BD}$ = 160°, what is the m$\widehat{AC}$?

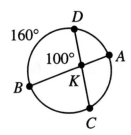

A   20°
B   40°
C   130°
D   260°

32. Given: m∠ABC = 130°, $\overleftrightarrow{CE}$ is a tangent, and $\overline{AB}$ is a chord, what is the m$\widehat{AB}$?

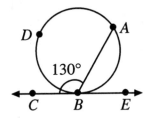

F   25°
G   50°
H   65°
J   100°

33. How far does the tip of an 8-inch minute hand on a clock travel in 15 minutes?

A   125.6 inches
B   50.24 inches
C   25.12 inches
D   12.56 inches

THREE-DIMENSIONAL FIGURES
(G.12, G.13)

34. Which two figures are different views of the same rectangular solid?

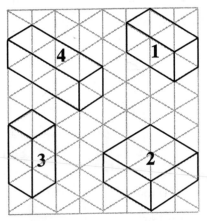

F   1 and 2
G   2 and 3
H   3 and 4
J   1 and 3

215

35. What is the surface area of this regular hexagonal pyramid?

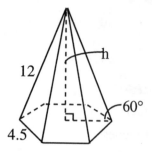

12
h
60°
4.5

A   81
B   162
C   243
D   324

36. Barbara packs a square based pyramid candle in a box with the same base and height. What is the volume of the packing material needed to fill the box?

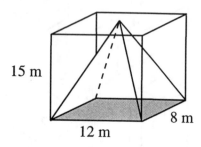

15 m
12 m
8 m

F   480 m³
G   960 m³
H   1080 m³
J   1440 m³

37. You are designing a label for a canned product. What is the area of the label to the nearest tenth of a centimeter?

3.25 cm
19 cm
SOUP

A   123.5 cm²
B   193.9 cm²
C   387.8 cm²
D   630.2 cm²

PROPORTIONAL REASONING
(G.14)

38. A road map of Virginia is drawn with a scale of 3 inches = 40 miles. Two cities are $13\frac{3}{4}$ inches apart on the map. What is the actual straight-line distance between the two cities?

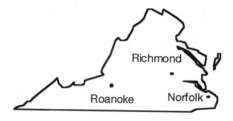

Richmond
Roanoke   Norfolk

F $173\frac{1}{3}$ miles

G $183\frac{1}{3}$ miles

H $223\frac{1}{3}$ miles

J   550 miles

39. Rectangles *ABCD* and *AEFG* are similar. The m$\overline{CD}$ = 5.6, the m$\overline{BC}$ = 11.8, and the m$\overline{AG}$ = 2.8. What is the measure of $\overline{AE}$?

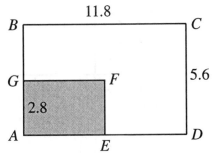

A   2.95
B   5.9
C   13.3
D   23.6

COORDINATE RELATIONS, TRANSFORMATIONS, AND VECTORS
(G.2, G.15)

40. Use the diagram below. What is the area of △*BAT* in square units?

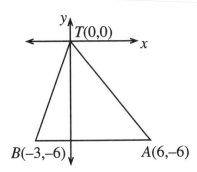

F   54
G   27
H   18
J   9

41. In parallelogram *ABCD*, the coordinates of three of the vertices are *A* (−1, −2), *B*(5, −2), and *C* (−3, 2). What are the coordinates of vertex D?

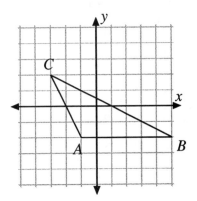

A   *D* (3, 2)
B   *D* (3, −2)
C   *D* (−3, 2)
D   *D* (2, 3)

42. What is the image of *E* after a 90° clockwise rotation about point *P*?

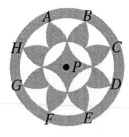

F   *B*
G   *C*
H   *H*
J   *G*

217

43. What are the coordinates of the image of $\triangle ABC$ under the translation $\langle 4, -3 \rangle$?

$$\begin{array}{c} \quad A \quad B \quad C \\ \begin{array}{c} x \\ y \end{array} \begin{bmatrix} -2 & 2 & 4 \\ -1 & -5 & 2 \end{bmatrix} \end{array}$$

A $\begin{bmatrix} 2 & 8 & 6 \\ -4 & -8 & -1 \end{bmatrix}$

B $\begin{bmatrix} -4 & -8 & -1 \\ 2 & 6 & 8 \end{bmatrix}$

C $\begin{bmatrix} 2 & 6 & 8 \\ -4 & -8 & -1 \end{bmatrix}$

D $\begin{bmatrix} 2 & 8 & 6 \\ -4 & -1 & -8 \end{bmatrix}$

44. Given: $\vec{u} = \begin{bmatrix} 2 \\ -2 \end{bmatrix}$ and $\vec{v}\begin{bmatrix} 3 \\ 1 \end{bmatrix}$. What is $\vec{u} + 2\vec{v}$?

F $\begin{bmatrix} 8 \\ 4 \end{bmatrix}$

G $\begin{bmatrix} 7 \\ 4 \end{bmatrix}$

H $\begin{bmatrix} 7 \\ 0 \end{bmatrix}$

J $\begin{bmatrix} 8 \\ 0 \end{bmatrix}$

45. Which column matrix represents the resultant vector for the sum of $\vec{u}$ and $\vec{v}$ in the graph below?

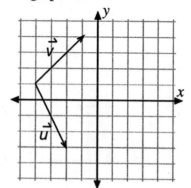

A $\begin{bmatrix} 0 \\ 1 \end{bmatrix}$

B $\begin{bmatrix} 1 \\ -1 \end{bmatrix}$

C $\begin{bmatrix} 5 \\ -1 \end{bmatrix}$

D $\begin{bmatrix} -6 \\ -1 \end{bmatrix}$

Geometry End-of-Course Formula Sheet

Key:	B = base	h = height	r = radius	s = side	Use 3.14 or $\frac{22}{7}$ for π

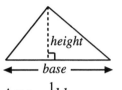

Area = $\frac{1}{2}bh$

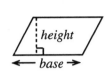

Area = $\frac{1}{2}h(b_1 + b_2)$

Area = bh

$V = \frac{4}{3}\pi r^3$

S.A. = $4\pi r^2$

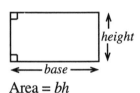

Area = bh

Area = πr^2

Circumference = $\pi 2r$

Pythagorean Theorem

$c^2 = a^2 + b^2$

Key:	V = volume	s = slant height	B = base area	P = base perimeter
	L.A. = Lateral Area		S.A. = Surface Area	

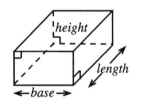

V = Bh

L.A. = Ph

S.A. = $2B + Ph$

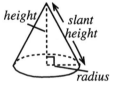

V = $\frac{1}{3}\pi r^2 h$

L.A. = $\pi r s$

S.A. = $\pi r^2 + \pi r s$

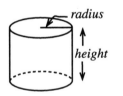

V = $\pi r^2 h$

L.A. = $2\pi r h$

S.A. = $2\pi r h + 2\pi r^2$

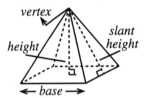

V = $\frac{1}{3}B h$

L.A. = $\frac{1}{2}P s$

S.A. = $B + \frac{1}{2}P s$

Geometric Symbols

Example	Reads
$\angle A$	angle A
m$\angle A$	measure of angle A
$\overline{AB}$	line segment AB
$\overleftrightarrow{AB}$	line AB
$\triangle ABC$	triangle ABC
AB	measure of line segment AB
$\overleftrightarrow{AB} \parallel \overleftrightarrow{CD}$	line AB is parallel to line CD

Example	Reads
$\overleftrightarrow{AB} \perp \overleftrightarrow{CD}$	line AB is perpendicular to line CD
$\angle A \cong \angle B$	angle A is congruent to angle B
$\triangle A \sim \triangle B$	triangle A is similar to triangle B
$\overarc{AB}$	arc AB
$\overrightarrow{AB}$	vector AB

219